MOVING MATH FORWARD THROUGH CRITICAL THINKING AND EXPLORATION

Shape Up

Focusing on Triangles, Transformations and Measurement

M. Katherine Gavin

Linda Jensen Sheffield

Suzanne H. Chapin

Kendall Hunt
publishing company

ACKNOWLEDGMENTS

Math Innovations Writing Team

Authors
M. Katherine Gavin

Linda Jensen Sheffield

Suzanne H. Chapin

Project Manager
Janice M. Vuolo

Teacher Edition Team
Ann Marie Spinelli

Nancy Anderson

Alice J. Gabbard

Jennifer M. MacPherson

Writing Assistants
Kathy Dorkin

Jane Paulin

Jacob J. Whitmore

Mathematics Editor
Kathleen G. Snook

Assessment Specialist
Nancy Anderson

Advisory Board
Jerry P. Becker

Janet Beissinger

Diane J. Briars

Ann Lawrence

Ira J. Papick

Cover image of white trianglular structure ©Corbis. Other cover images, other than female model, used under license by ShutterStock, Inc. Table of Trigonometry on p. 78 public domain; originally from 1728 Cyclopaedia, Volume 2. Photos on pp. 3, 74 and 78 copyright Kendall Hunt Publishing. All other interior photos used under license by ShutterStock, Inc.

Kendall Hunt
publishing company

www.kendallhunt.com

Send all inquiries to:

4050 Westmark Drive

Dubuque, IA 52004-1840

1-800-542-6657

| Production Date: 2015 |
| Printed by: LSI |
| United States of America |
| Batch number: 431248 |

Printed in the United States of America

1 2 3 4 5 6 7 8 9 10   16 15 14 13

Shape Up: Focusing on Triangles, Transformations and Measurement

Table of Contents

UNIT GOALS

Shape Up: Focusing on Triangles, Transformations and Measurement

After studying this unit, you should be able to:

- Find measures of angles formed by parallel lines and a transversal.
- Understand, prove and use the Triangle Sum Theorem.
- Find unknown measures of angles inside and outside triangles and other polygons.
- Show that two triangles are congruent using properties and transformations.
- Understand and use properties of similar triangles, including the use of dilations, rotations, reflections and translations.
- Work with and develop formulas for the volume of cylinders, cones and spheres.

Dear Student Mathematician,

In *Shape Up*, you will take on the role of an employee in the firm Accent on Architecture. At times you will be the architect on a new project. Other times you will be the construction contractor. In both jobs you will be working with the designs of new structures, focusing on the use of triangles and other shapes to add form, function and detail to buildings.

In this unit, you will find the measures of angles formed when two parallel lines are intersected by another line. You will then use this information to prove the Triangle Sum Theorem. You have actually seen and used this theorem before. It states that the sum of the angle measures in a triangle is 180°. You will use different transformations to create congruent and similar figures. You will see how these transformations can create beautiful artistic designs to enhance buildings and craft projects. Finally, you will explore the volume of solids with curved surfaces—cylinders, cones and spheres—and look at the relationships among them. You will learn how volume is an important consideration for architects and contractors.

We hope you enjoy the activities and that you become better mathematicians by solving interesting geometry problems. You may even be inspired to think about a career as an architect!

Mathematically Yours,
The Authors

M. Katherine Gavin   *Linda Sheffield*   *Suzanne H. Chapin*

Exploring Angles

Have you ever looked at the framework for a roof? Maybe you have seen exposed beams in a garage, a restaurant or a factory. What you see is a set of perfectly parallel support beams running from the bottom of the roofline to the top of the structure. How do the carpenters know the precise angle to cut each board? Mathematics comes into play.

Taking a Closer Look: Angles and Parallel Lines

 Start It Off

Ben's little brother, Tucker, was watching him draw angles with his protractor. He said he could pick out the bigger angle. He pointed to the angle on the left and smiled. Unfortunately, Ben had to burst his bubble and explain that the angles are actually the same size. Help Ben explain to Tucker how that could be.

Roof Lines and Angles

The outline of the front of a garage is shown on the next page. The angles (angles 2 and 5 in the figures below) of the support beams must match the angle of the roofline. Notice that the dotted line going straight down the middle of the front of the garage is parallel to the sides of the garage.

1. a) Without measuring, put the four marked angles in each of the figures below in order according to what you think their measures are, from smallest to largest.

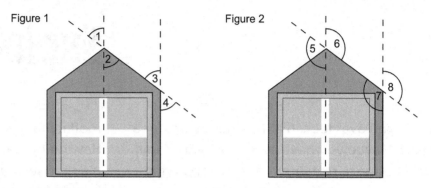

Figure 1

Figure 2

b) Use a protractor to measure the marked angles in Figure 1. What did you find?

c) Now measure the marked angles in Figure 2. What did you find?

Vertical Angles

When two lines intersect, they form four angles. Angles that have the same vertex and whose sides are opposite rays are called vertical angles. Angles 1 and 2 in Figure 1 above are vertical angles.

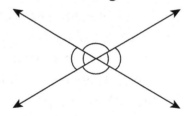

NOTE Be careful to spell *vertical* correctly. It is NOT *verticle*—a common misspelling. And, by the way, we are talking about angles, not angels—those are the creatures with wings!

2. a) Name the remaining vertical angles in Figures 1 and 2 above. Are they congruent (having the same size, shape and measure)?

b) Are vertical angles always congruent? Make a prediction.

c) Use AngLegs™ to make several different pairs of intersecting lines. Measure the vertical angles.

d) Was your prediction from Part b correct? Draw a conclusion.

Supplementary Angles

MATHEMATICALLY SPEAKING

▶ **straight angle**

▶ **supplementary angles**

 **Let's Review**

A straight angle is an angle formed by two rays with the same endpoint and pointing in opposite directions. The rays of a straight angle form a line. The measure of a straight angle is 180°. For example, $\angle ABC$ below is a straight angle.

$$\overset{\longleftarrow}{\underset{A}{}\qquad\qquad\underset{B}{\bullet}\qquad\qquad\underset{C}{}}\overset{\longrightarrow}{}$$

Notice that two angles whose sum is 180° are called **supplementary angles**.

In the drawings below, $\angle 1$ and $\angle 2$ are supplementary and $\angle 3$ and $\angle 4$ are supplementary, so the sum of the measures of each pair is 180°.

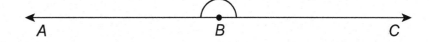

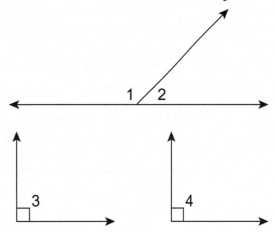

3. Using Lesson Guide 1.1: *Looking for Supplementary Angles*, find all the supplementary angles in Figures 1 and 2 from Question 1.

Parallel Lines and Angles

4. **a)** Use the lines on a piece of notebook paper to draw a pair of parallel lines. Label the lines *l* and *m*. We can denote parallel lines by writing, "line *l* ∥ line *m*." We can indicate that two lines in a drawing are parallel by marking a double arrow (>>) on both, as shown in the diagram below.

   b) A transversal is a line that crosses two or more lines. Draw a transversal crossing your parallel lines that is not perpendicular to the lines. Check with a partner to make sure your transversals look different. Label the transversal *t*.

   c) Label the angles on your paper with numbers, as shown below.

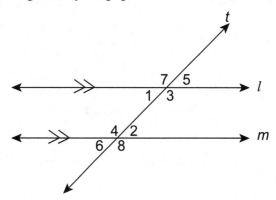

There are special angle relationships formed when two parallel lines are cut by a transversal.

5. **a)** Based on the measurements you did earlier with Figures 1 and 2, predict which of the angles in your drawing are congruent.

   b) Measure the angles with a protractor and see if you are correct.

   c) Name all pairs of congruent angles.

   d) Which of your congruent pairs are vertical angles?

   e) Are there any supplementary angles in your drawing? If so, name them.

    **Hint**
   See page 154

   f) Did your partner find the same relationships among the numbered angles?

6. Draw a parallelogram on your lined notebook paper. Use a thin piece of spaghetti as your transversal. (You may want to tape the spaghetti down.) Number your angles as shown below.

   a) Predict which pairs of angles will be congruent.

   b) Measure the numbered angles and record the measurements in row 1 of the table below.

   c) Were your predictions correct?

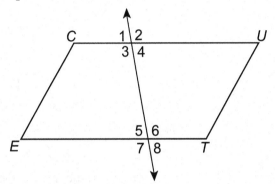

	m∠1	m∠2	m∠3	m∠4	m∠5	m∠6	m∠7	m∠8
Transversal 1								
Transversal 2								
Transversal 3								

7. Now move your transversal so that it still intersects both parallel lines, but at a different angle. Work with your partner to answer the following questions.

   a) Do you think the measures of the angles stay the same? Why or why not?

   b) Do you think the relationships among the pairs of angles stay the same? Why or why not?

   c) Measure the angles and record the measurements in row 2. Were your predictions correct?

   d) Move your transversal again so that it goes through the two other parallel lines that make up the parallelogram. Make predictions about the relationships among the angles. Then, measure the angles and record the measurements in row 3.

You should have found many pairs of congruent angles in your explorations. Some of these are vertical angles. There are more pairs that have special names, too. Using the diagram below, we can identify several types of congruent angles formed when a transversal crosses two parallel lines.

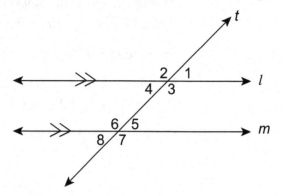

MATHEMATICALLY SPEAKING

▶ alternate interior angles

▶ alternate exterior angles

▶ same-side interior angles

- $\angle 3 \cong \angle 6$ and $\angle 4 \cong \angle 5$. These pairs of angles are called alternate interior angles. They are inside the two parallel lines (interior) and on opposite (alternate) sides of the transversal.

- $\angle 1 \cong \angle 5$, $\angle 2 \cong \angle 6$, $\angle 3 \cong \angle 7$, and $\angle 8 \cong \angle 4$. Each pair of angles in this group is on the same side of the transversal, but the angles are not next to each other. These pairs are called corresponding angles since they correspond to the same position at each intersection point (top right, bottom right, top left and bottom left).

- $\angle 1 \cong \angle 8$ and $\angle 2 \cong \angle 7$. These are called alternate exterior angles. They are on the outside of the parallel lines (exterior), and they are on opposite (alternate) sides of the transversal.

There are also supplementary angles. Some of these form a straight angle. Others do not.

Two angles that are on the same side of the transversal and are inside the parallel lines are called same-side interior angles. In our drawing, these angles are $\angle 3$ and $\angle 5$ as well as $\angle 4$ and $\angle 6$. Same-side interior angles are supplementary.

8. Using the roofline drawing in Figure 1, name the types of angles in each pair:

   a) angles 1 and 2

   b) angles 1 and 3

   c) angles 2 and 3

   d) angles 2 and 4

   e) angles 3 and 4

   f) angles 1 and 4

Up to this point, we have talked about angles made with parallel lines cut by a transversal. What about the angles formed by two non-parallel lines cut by a transversal?

9. Using AngLegs™, investigate to see if any of the angles formed by a transversal cutting two non-parallel lines are congruent. Here is one example.

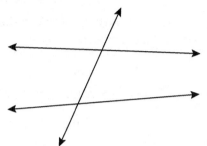

 **W**rap It Up _____

Talk to your partner. How would you explain the difference between corresponding angles and alternate interior angles to Cooper, who was absent? Make sure to mention where you might find these types of angles. Now, share with the class.

On Your Own

 **Write About It**

1. List all congruent angles formed when two parallel lines are cut by a transversal. Draw a diagram, number the angles, and identify the pairs.

2. Abdul told Keira that supplementary angles are two adjacent angles that form a straight line. Keira said that the opposite angles of a square are supplementary, but they are not adjacent. Who is correct?

3. Name all the vertical angles in this diagram.

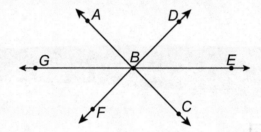

? Hint
See page 154

4. Fill in the blanks with *sometimes*, *always* or *never*.

   a) Vertical angles are _____ congruent.

   b) Supplementary angles are _____ congruent.

   c) Vertical angles are _____ adjacent.

   d) Supplementary angles are _____ adjacent.

5. Name all the supplementary angles in rectangle *MATH* below.

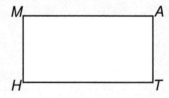

6. a) In parallelogram *ABCD*, which angles are supplementary? Explain.

   ? Hint
   See page 154

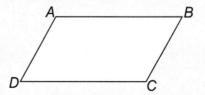

b) Draw diagonal $\overline{AC}$. Which angles formed by this diagonal are congruent? Explain.

7. In the figure below, line $k \parallel$ line p and m$\angle 1 = 65°$. Find the measures of all the other numbered angles and state a reason for each. Include the angle names and types.

For example: m$\angle 2 = 65°$, because $\angle 1$ and $\angle 2$ are alternate interior angles formed by two parallel lines and a transversal, and alternate interior angles are equal in measure.

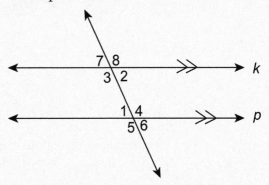

8. Line $c \parallel$ line d. m$\angle 3 = 100°$. Find the measures of all the other numbered angles and give a reason for each.

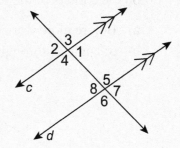

9. Line h is parallel to line j and line t is parallel to line s and m$\angle 6$ is $54°$. Find the measures of all numbered angles and give a reason for each.

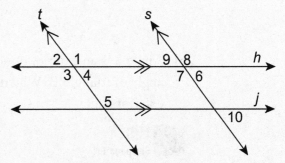

10. The bridge for the Route 100 overpass must be replaced. Your job is to precisely measure the angles of intersection before the work begins. If m∠1 is 110° and Routes 9 North and South are parallel, what properties would you use to determine the measures of ∠5, ∠8 and ∠4? Find the measure of each angle. Explain your reasoning.

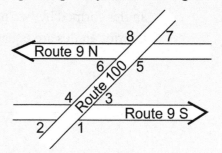

11. The bridge in Question 10 is moved, and ∠1 now measures 100°. Find the measures of all the other angles.

12. As a landscape architect in the Accent on Architecture firm , you have been hired to create a geometric garden. You've installed flower beds *A* and *B*, each of which has three 60° angles. The red bricks on the corners of the rectangular grass area are squares.

    a) Before more work can be done, you need to determine the measures of angles 1 through 4. Find these measures and a reason for each.

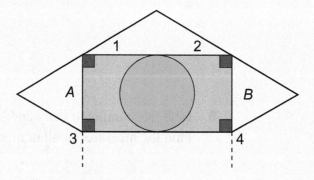

    b) Angle 3 is an exterior angle of triangle A, and angle 4 is an exterior angle of triangle B. Why do you think these angles are called exterior angles?

    ? Hint
    See page 154

13. Judy tells Josh that none of the angles in the diagram are congruent. She says that congruent angles are formed only when parallel lines are cut by a transversal. Line *a* is not parallel to line *b*, so there are no pairs of congruent angles. Do you agree with Judy? Explain.

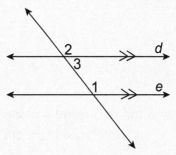

14. Line *d* ∥ line *e*. m∠1 is *x*°. m∠2 is $(2x - 140)°$. Find the measures of ∠1, ∠2 and ∠3. Show your work and explain your reasoning.

15. As the construction contractor for Accent on Architecture 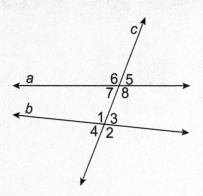, you are building a new model house. You are installing wooden studs, or posts, to create the bedroom walls on the second floor. You know that installing the wall studs perpendicular to the floor boards will make sure that these wall studs are parallel to each other. Explain mathematically why this is true.

Think Back

16. While she was at summer camp, Erica sent one piece of mail to her parents daily for 14 days. It costs $0.46 to mail a letter and $0.33 to mail a postcard. If she sent 8 letters, find out how much it cost to purchase all the stamps for the letters and the postcards.

17. Find the area of a circle (to the nearest hundredth) whose circumference is 6π cm. Use 3.14 for π.

18. If $\sqrt{x} = 4$, then $x = $ _____.

    A. 2

    B. 16

    C. 8

    D. 2.5

19. List the dimensions for all rectangular prisms that have whole-number side lengths and a volume of 12 cubic units.

20. a) Give the surface area for each of the rectangular prisms you listed in Question 19.

    b) Explain the difference between volume and surface area.

LESSON 1.2 The Triangle Sum Theorem

→ **Start It Off**

Use the clues below and logical thinking to figure out who won the race.

- Three horses named Tri, Quad and Hex ran in a race.
- Fee, Fi and Foe each owned one of the horses.
- Fi's horse nearly won.
- This was Tri's third race.
- The white horse was owned by Foe.
- The horse owned by Fee was in its first race.
- Quad never made it out of the starting gate.
- The horse that won was black.

1. Name the winning horse.

2. Name the owner of the winning horse.

3. Were you using inductive or deductive reasoning to figure out the answer? Explain.

Add 'em Up

Now we are going to study the angles in triangles. You know that there are lots of different types of triangles, but they all have three angles and three sides.

MATHEMATICALLY SPEAKING

▶ Triangle Sum Theorem

 NOTE There is something else all triangles have in common. It is an important theorem called the Triangle Sum Theorem.
The sum of the measures of the angles in any triangle is 180°.

1. **a)** Explain how you can show that the sum of the angles in any triangle is 180°.

   b) Now share your ideas with a partner.

   c) Together, come up with at least two different ways. Share your ideas with the class.

2. Discuss the following with a partner and then share with the class.

a) José, Jean and Jolene measured the angles of three different triangles. They found a pattern and said the sum of the three angles of a triangle is 180°. Have they proven this is true for all triangles? Why or why not?

b) What type of reasoning were they using?

c) How does their reasoning compare with the reasoning you used in the Start It Off problem?

Proving the Triangle Sum Theorem

Now we will use a mathematical proof to show that the Triangle Sum Theorem is true.

MATHEMATICALLY SPEAKING

▶ proof

A proof is a logical argument that shows why a statement must be true.

3. a) Draw *any* type of triangle and label the vertices *A, B* and *C*.

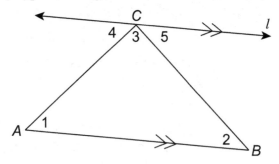

b) Next, draw line *l* through vertex *C*, parallel to $\overline{AB}$. Number the angles as shown.

c) Using what you learned in Lesson 1.1, gather some information about the measures of the angles and their relationships to one another without actually measuring the angles.

Hint
See page 154

d) Can you justify that m∠1 + m∠2 + m∠3 = 180°? Explain.

e) What type of reasoning did you use in Part d? Did you show that the Triangle Sum Theorem is true for all triangles?

f) How did this type of reasoning compare to the one you used in the Start It Off?

When mathematicians discover a proof, they write it down in a logical, step-by-step manner. They explain each step and use mathematical reasoning to justify it. Sometimes proofs are put in a two-column format as shown below. This is a good example of how to use deductive reasoning.

4. Fill in the blank boxes in Steps 2, 3 and 4 to complete the formal proof of the Triangle Sum Theorem.

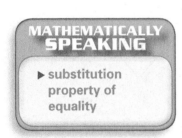
NOTE In this proof, we will use the substitution property of equality. This property states that if two quantities are equal, they can be substituted for one another in any expression.

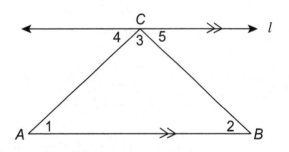

Statement	Justification
1. △ABC is drawn with line *l* through *C* and parallel to $\overline{AB}$.	**1.** Given **NOTE** Mathematicians use "given" in proofs to indicate information that is stated in the problem.
2. m∠4 + m∠3 + m∠5 = 180°	**2.**
3. ∠1 ≅ ∠4	**3.**
4. ∠2 ≅ ∠5	**4.**
5. So m∠ _____ + m∠3 + m∠ _____ = 180°	**5.** The substitution property of equality. (Angles with measures equal to the angles in Step 2 have been substituted into the equation.)

You have now proven that the sum of the measures of the angles in any triangle is 180°.

5. Determine the missing angle measures below.
Explain how you arrived at your answers.

a)

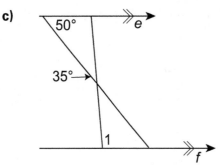

65°

1   20°

b)

1

60°

c)

50° $\gg e$

35°

1

f

d)

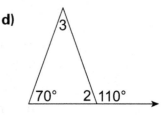

3

70°   2 110°

e)

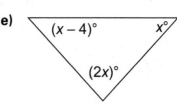

$(x-4)°$ $x°$

$(2x)°$

6. Tyrone thinks that if three angles of one triangle are congruent to three angles of another triangle, then the two triangles are congruent, (in other words, they are the same size and shape). Do you agree? Explain.

7. The Accent on Architecture designers are creating an atrium on the first floor of their latest office building project. The atrium has a water garden, as shown in the diagram below. Find the measures of angles 1, 2 and 3.

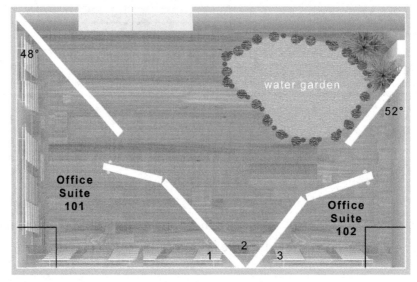

8. Find the measure of each of the numbered angles below.

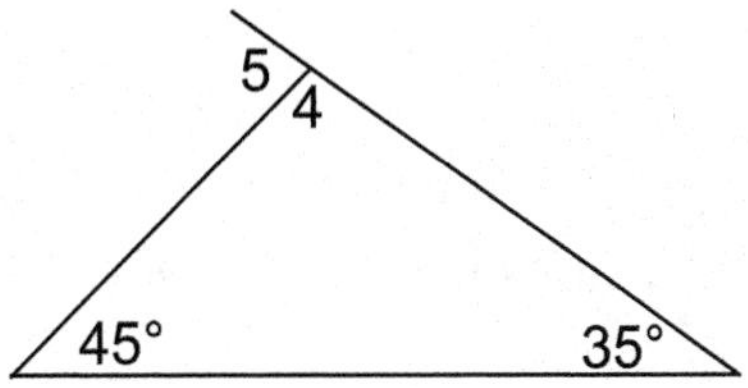

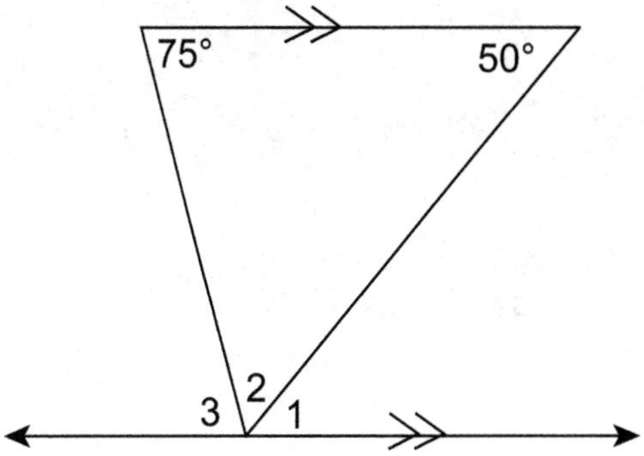

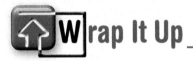

Wrap It Up

How is a proof different from a generalization formed using inductive reasoning?

MATHEMATICALLY SPEAKING

- proof
- substitution property of equality
- Triangle Sum Theorem

Write
About It

1. Using the diagram to the right, prove that the sum of the angle measures in △*KIN* is 180°.

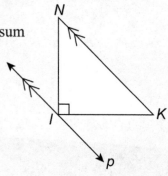

2. Prove that the sum of the measures of the angles of any quadrilateral is 360°.

? **Hint**
See page 154

3. Find the measure of angle *A* in each triangle. Is there more than one possible value? How do you know? (The tick marks on the sides of a figure indicate the sides are congruent, or equal in measure.)

a)
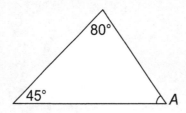

d)

b)

e)
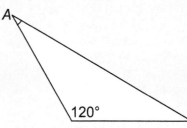

c)
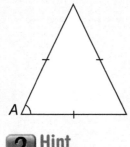

f)
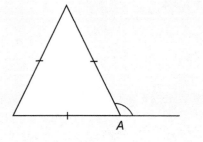

? **Hint**
See page 154

4. Find the value of *x*.

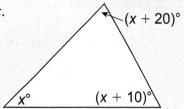

5. a) Fill in the table below. Explain how you arrived at your answers.

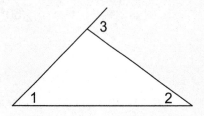

∠1	20°	45°	38°	
∠2	70°		65°	75°
∠3		115°		120°

b) How can you find m∠3 using m∠1 and m∠2?

6. In Question 5, ∠3 is one of the exterior angles of the triangle.

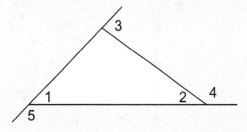

a) Find the measures of exterior angles 4 and 5 for each of the triangles in the table in Question 5.

b) Find the sum of the measures of the exterior angles for the triangles in the table in Question 5.

c) Make a conjecture about the sum of the measures of the exterior angles of any triangle.

Think Beyond

7. Find the measures of *x*, *y* and *z*.

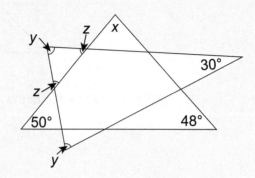

8. If line *a* is parallel to line *b*, which of the following is *not* a true statement?

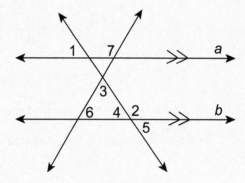

   A. $\angle 1 \cong \angle 5$

   B. $\angle 2$ and $\angle 4$ are supplementary.

   C. $\angle 7 \cong \angle 6$

   D. $m\angle 6 = 180 - (m\angle 3 + m\angle 4)$

Think Beyond

9. Write a formal proof to prove if two angles of one triangle are congruent to two angles of another, then the third angles of the triangles must also be congruent. This is sometimes called the Third Angle Theorem.

10. Sofia divided a 40-foot line segment into three parts so that the first part is 4 feet shorter than the second, and the second part is 7 feet longer than the third. How long is each piece?

11. What is the value of the expression below?

$$\frac{4 \cdot 3}{9 - 8 \div 2 \cdot 3}$$

12. The area, A, of a trapezoid is given by $A = \frac{1}{2} ha + \frac{1}{2} hb$, where a and b are the lengths of the parallel sides and h is the height. If $h = 7$, $a = 3$ and $b = 5$, which of the following is the area of the trapezoid? You might sketch the trapezoid to help you.

  A. 11 square units

  B. $1\frac{5}{2}$ square units

  C. 28 square units

  D. 56 square units

13. If a polygon has exactly two right angles, what is the fewest number of sides it could have? Name a possible shape.

14. I have a bag of 36 M&M's®, including 7 reds, 8 blues, 3 yellows and other colors.

What is the ratio of red : yellow? _____

red : not red? _____

blue : not blue? _____

If I reach in the bag, what is the probability of getting a blue M&M®?

_____

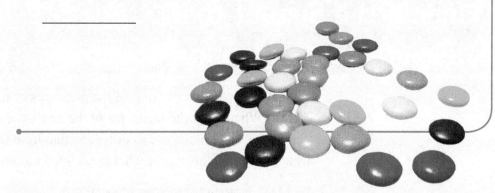

Oh, the Things You Can Do with the Triangle Sum Theorem!

 Start It Off

MATHEMATICALLY SPEAKING

▶ interior angle (of a polygon)

Kristi knows that a rectangle is a quadrilateral with four right angles, and so the sum of the interior angle measures of a rectangle is 360°. An **interior angle** of a polygon is an angle inside the polygon formed by two sides. She wonders if the sum of the interior angle measures of any quadrilateral is 360°. To find out, she draws the irregular shapes below.

1. Are the shapes below quadrilaterals? How do you know?

2. Measure the angles. Do the measures add up to 360°?

3. Does this show that all quadrilaterals have angle measures that sum to 360°? Explain.

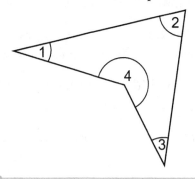   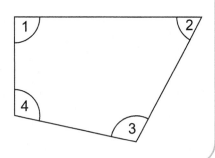

Finding the Sum of the Measures of Angles in Polygons

You have proven that the sum of the measures of the angles of any triangle is 180°. What about the measures of the angles of other polygons? Is the sum of the angle measures of polygons that have the same number of sides always the same, no matter what the polygon looks like?

1. Make a prediction. Now let's explore.

2. In groups, choose a particular type of polygon to explore (for example, pentagons or octagons).

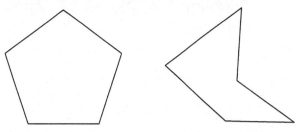

a) Each person in your group should draw a different version of the polygon you have chosen, so that no two polygons are congruent. Make sure some are irregular polygons (all sides and all angles are not congruent) like the ones Kristi drew in the Start It Off.

b) Measure each of the interior angles in your polygon and find the sum of all the measures.

c) Compare your findings with others in your group. Take into account the lack of precision with protractors.

d) Make a conjecture about the sum of the interior angles of the chosen polygon.

3. In a chart similar to the one below, fill in the class conjectures from Question 2. Look for patterns.

Polygon	Number of Sides	Sum of the Interior Angle Measure
Triangle	3	
Quadrilateral	4	

4. a) What type of reasoning were you using when you looked for patterns?

b) How could you disprove your conjecture?

5. Now let's use the Triangle Sum Theorem to find a formula that can be used to find the sum of the angle measures in a polygon with any number of sides. Complete the chart on the next page, drawing as many diagonals as possible from *one* of the vertices of the polygon. This creates triangles on the interior of the polygon.

Shape	Number of Sides	Number of Triangles	Sum of the Measures of the Interior Angles
Triangle	3	 1	1(180) = 180°
Quadrilateral	4	2	2(180) = 360°
Pentagon	5	3	
Hexagon			
Octagon			
Decagon			
Polygon of n sides	n		

6. Using the rule you discovered for a polygon with *n* sides, find the sum of the measures of the interior angles in a dodecagon.

 Hint
See page 154

See page 154

7. If the sum of the angles in a polygon is 2,700°, how many sides does the polygon have?

MATHEMATICALLY
SPEAKING

▶ regular polygon

8. In a regular polygon, the lengths of the sides are all equal and the measures of the angles are all equal. Find the measures of the interior angles in:

   a) a regular quadrilateral

   b) a regular pentagon

   c) a regular hexagon

   d) a regular octagon

   e) a regular decagon

9. Explain how to find the measure of each interior angle of any regular polygon.

 **Think Beyond**

10. How does inventor Chuck Hoberman use the properties of polygons you have just learned? Find out the answer at the Futures website: www.thefutureschannel.com/dockets/hands-on_math/inventing_with_polygons/.

 **Wrap It Up**

Explain how to find the sum of the angles in any polygon using the Triangle Sum Theorem.

MATHEMATICALLY SPEAKING

▶ interior angle (of a polygon)

▶ regular polygon

Write About It

1. Write a proof to justify that the sum of the interior angles in a pentagon is 540°.

2. Find the sum of the angles in an icosagon (a polygon with 20 sides).

3. Which formula can be used to find the measure of each interior angle of an n-sided regular polygon?

   A. $180(n + 2)$

   B. $\dfrac{180(n + 2)}{n}$

   C. $\dfrac{180(n - 2)}{n}$

   D. $360n$

4. What do we call a regular quadrilateral? Explain your answer.

5. How many sides does a regular polygon have if each interior angle measures 160°?

6. What's wrong in the diagram below? (The hash marks indicate that $\angle B$ is congruent to $\angle D$.)

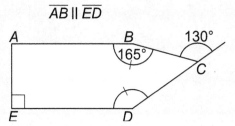

$$\overline{AB} \parallel \overline{ED}$$

7. At , you are designing a new home and looking at the types of tiles to install in the kitchen. The owner would like something other than square or rectangular tiles. You want to use tiles that are shaped like regular polygons and that fit together, without gaps or overlaps. Can you use triangles? Pentagons? Hexagons? Explain your answer.

   ? Hint
   See page 154

8. The design for the new house at  calls for an octagonal window. Window grills will be installed at right angles and perpendicular to the sides of the window, as shown below. The octagonal window is a regular polygon.

a) What is the shape of each of the four figures formed by the window grills?

b) Find the measure of each interior angle in one of these four figures.

9. Mike found that the sum of the interior angle measures of a pentagon is 540°. Manny said that if that is true, then the sum of the angle measures of a decagon must be 2 · 540° or 1,080°, since a decagon has twice as many angles. Do you agree with Manny? Explain.

10. a) Draw a regular quadrilateral, pentagon and hexagon along with their exterior angles at each vertex.

b) Find the sum of the measures of the exterior angles for each shape.

c) Make a conjecture about the sum of the exterior angles of a regular polygon.

d) Try out your conjecture on an irregular polygon. Does it work?

Think Back

11. A truck driver travels 340 miles, averaging no less than 55 mph and no more than 68 mph. Write an inequality for t, the amount of time the trip might have taken.

12. What is the difference between the mean and median of the test scores in the table below?

Name	Test Score
Lina	83
Alex	68
Walker	82
Tim	89
Naomi	95
Kyle	91
Victoria	82
Thomas	90
Briana	85
Michaela	70

13. If $\frac{1}{4}$ of a certain number is 2.5, what is the number?

14. While sorting melons, Melanie found 27 less than $\frac{2}{3}$ of them were defective. If 45 were in good condition, how many were defective?

15. Determine the lengths of sides a and b shown below.

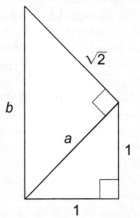

Optional Technology Lesson for this section available in your eBook

Sum It Up

In this section you proved the Triangle Sum Theorem. To do this, first you had to learn about the relationships in the measure of the angles formed when two parallel lines are cut by a transversal. You realized how powerful the Triangle Sum Theorem is by using it to explore angle measures of other polygons.

Parallel Lines and Transversals

When two parallel lines are cut by a transversal, the angles formed have the following relationships:

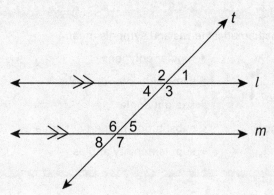

- ∠3 ≅ ∠6 and ∠4 ≅ ∠5. These pairs are called **alternate interior angles.**

- ∠1 ≅ ∠5, ∠3 ≅ ∠7, ∠4 ≅ ∠8 and ∠2 ≅ ∠6. These pairs are called **corresponding angles.**

- ∠1 ≅ ∠8 and ∠2 ≅ ∠7. These pairs are called **alternate exterior angles.**

- ∠3 and ∠5, as well as ∠4 and ∠6, are called **same-side interior angles.** They are supplementary angles (the sum of their measure is 180°).

- ∠1 and ∠2 are adjacent angles that are also supplementary since they form a straight angle. There are other pairs of supplementary angles in the diagram. Can you name them?

- ∠1 ≅ ∠4, ∠2 ≅ ∠3, ∠5 ≅ ∠8 and ∠6 ≅ ∠7. These pairs are called **vertical angles.**

The Triangle Sum Theorem

- The **Triangle Sum Theorem** states that the sum of the measures of the interior angles in a triangle is 180°.

Polygon Angles

- The sum of the measures of the interior angles in a polygon of n sides is $180(n - 2)$.

- Each interior angle of an n-sided regular polygon (polygon whose sides are equal length and whose angles all equal the same measure) has the measure $\frac{180(n - 2)}{n}$.

MATHEMATICALLY SPEAKING

Do you know what these mathematical terms and symbols mean?

▶ alternate exterior angles

▶ alternate interior angles

▶ congruent ($\cong$)

▶ interior angles (of a polygon)

▶ proof

▶ regular polygon

▶ same-side interior angles

▶ straight angle

▶ substitution property of equality

▶ supplementary angles

▶ symbol "$\parallel$"

▶ transversal

▶ Triangle Sum Theorem

▶ vertical angles

Part 1. What did you learn?

1. In triangle *ABC*, m∠*A* = 62°. If ∠*A* ≅ ∠*B*, then m∠*B* = _____°
   and m∠*C* = _____°.

2. In isosceles triangle *DEF*, ∠*D* ≅ ∠*E* and m∠*F* = 120°.
   So, m∠*D* = m∠*E* = _____°.

3. In the following diagram, lines *m* and *n* are parallel and
   m∠3 = 120°. Use this information to complete the chart
   below the diagram.

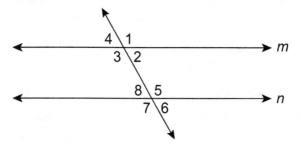

	Type of Angle	Angles of this Type in the Diagram	Measure of Each Angle
a.	alternate exterior		
b.	alternate interior		
c.	corresponding angles		
d.	vertical angles		
e.	supplementary angles		
f.	same-side interior angles		

4. In the diagram below, m∠1 = 40°. Complete the missing information in the two-column proof to prove that the measure of m∠1 of trapezoid *ABCD* is 140°.

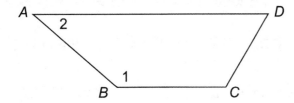

Statement	Justification
a. Shape *ABCD* is a trapezoid. The m∠2 = 40°.	**b.** Given
c. A trapezoid has exactly one pair of _____ sides.	**d.** Definition of trapezoid
e. ∠ _____ and the exterior angle at vertex *B* are _____ interior angles.	**f.** Because shape *ABCD* is a trapezoid, line *AB* can be thought of as a _____ that cuts the parallel lines _____ and _____.
g. The exterior angle at vertex *B* is congruent to ∠2, so it measures _____°.	**h.** Alternate _____ angles are congruent.
i. The exterior angle at vertex *B* and ∠1 are _____ angles, so their sum is _____°.	**j.** These two angles are _____ angles because they form a _____.
k. The measure of ∠1 is 140°.	**l.** The measure of a straight angle is _____. And _____ − _____ = 140°.

5. In the diagram below, lines *a* and *b* are parallel and the measure of angle 5 is *x°*. Use this information to fill in the blanks in the sentences below.

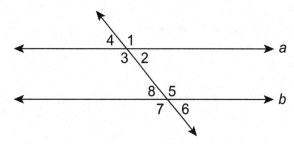

a. Angles 5 and 8 are supplementary angles, so the sum of their measures is _____°.

b. Since m∠5 = *x°*, the measure of ∠8 can be expressed as _____°.

c. m∠5 = m∠_____ = m∠_____ = m∠_____ = *x°*

d. m∠8 = m∠_____ = m∠_____ = m∠_____ = _____°

e. If m∠7 = 130°, then *x* = _____° because _____.

f. If m∠7 = 130°, then m∠8 = _____° because

_____.

6. Can a pair of vertical angles ever be supplementary angles? Why or why not?

7. Complete the missing entries in the chart below.

	Shape	Number of Sides	Number of Triangles	Sum of the Measures of the Angles
a.	Rhombus			
b.			3	
c.	Dodecagon	12		
d.	Polygon of *x* sides			

8. Use the chart from Question 7 to fill in the blanks below.

   a. The measure of each interior angle in a regular pentagon
   is _____°.

   b. The measure of each interior angle in a regular dodecagon
   is _____°.

Part 2. What went wrong?

9. Makio looked at the diagram below and said, "I know that ∠1
   measures 50°, but I don't have enough information to find any of
   the other angles." What is wrong with Makio's reasoning? What
   would you say or do to help him understand that you *can* find the
   measures of all eight angles by only knowing the measure
   of ∠1?

   In the diagram below, lines *m* and *n* are parallel.
   m∠1 = 50°.

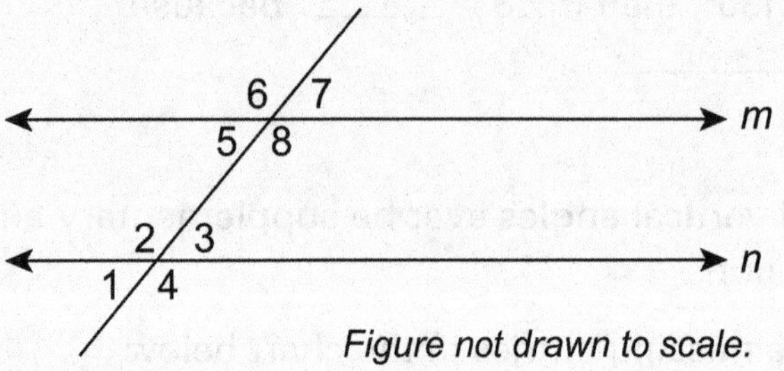

   6 7
   5 8   *m*

   2 3
   1 4   *n*

   Figure not drawn to scale.

10. Sonya found the interior angle sum of a hexagon by dividing the
    hexagon into 6 congruent triangles. She wrote, "The interior
    angle sum of a hexagon is 1,080° since 6 · 180° = 1,080°."

    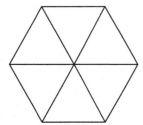

    What is wrong with Sonya's reasoning? What would you say or
    do to help her find the correct interior angle sum of a hexagon?

SECTION 2

Exploring Congruent and Similar Shapes Using Transformations

In Section 1, you looked at congruent angles and talked about how architects might use them. In this section, you will be exploring congruent and similar shapes. When do you think that architects might use these? Think about constructing symmetrical buildings and about the sketches that an architect makes when designing houses. If a building has a line of symmetry, the shapes on either side must be congruent. Architects use scale drawings and scale models to show their clients what their future houses will look like. The shapes and designs on these drawings are similar to what the actual shapes and designs will be. Maps are also a type of scale drawing. Mapmakers, called cartographers, make small images that show what large areas look like. In this section, you will explore congruence and similarity by examining special properties of triangles and by transforming, or moving, shapes in a plane.

LESSON 2.1 Congruent Triangles

 Start It Off

MATHEMATICALLY SPEAKING

- ▶ scalene triangle
- ▶ right triangle
- ▶ obtuse triangle
- ▶ acute triangle
- ▶ equiangular triangle
- ▶ equilateral triangle
- ▶ isosceles triangle

1. Use the terms below to classify each triangle. You may use more than one term if appropriate. Use your glossary if necessary.

scalene   acute   equilateral
right   equiangular   isosceles
obtuse

a.
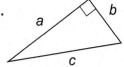

c.
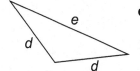

e.
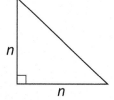

b.

d.
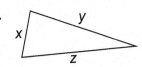

2. **a)** Which triangle can you use four terms to classify?

   b) Which of the above terms refer to the angles in a triangle?

   c) Which of the above terms refer to sides in a triangle?

Corresponding Parts of Congruent Triangles

MATHEMATICALLY SPEAKING

▶ corresponding sides

▶ corresponding angles

Two figures are congruent if they have the same size and shape. This means that if you put one figure on top of the other, they match up perfectly.

When we say that two figures must have the same shape, it does not mean that they are both triangles or both rectangles. For example, in the Start It Off, you looked at all the different types of triangles. None of the triangles were exactly the same shape, however.

In this lesson, you will determine if triangles are congruent using measurements of sides and angles. When comparing figures, the sides that are in the same relative position in each figure are called **corresponding sides**. The angles that are in the same relative position and have the same measure are called **corresponding angles**. If all corresponding sides are the same length and all corresponding angles have the same measure, then the polygons are congruent.

The triangles below are congruent.

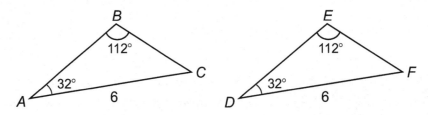

Triangle *ABC* is congruent to triangle *DEF*.

We say, "triangle *ABC* is congruent to triangle *DEF*." In this statement, the order in which we list the vertices in the triangle names is important. Vertices of corresponding angles must be in the same position in the names. In this case, angle *A* corresponds to angle *D*, angle *B* corresponds to angle *E*, and angle *C* corresponds to angle *F*. This also means that side *AB* corresponds to side *DE*, side *AC* corresponds to side *DF*, and so on.

When a triangle is said to be congruent to another triangle, it means that the corresponding parts of each triangle are congruent.

In the figure below, we say that triangle *ABC* is congruent to triangle *DEF* by writing △*ABC* ≅ △*DEF*.

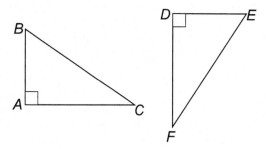

There are two ways to indicate congruent corresponding sides.

1) We can talk about the segments being congruent by writing $\overline{AB} \cong \overline{DE}$.

2) We can talk about the lengths being equal by writing $AB = DE$.

There are also two ways to name congruent corresponding angles.

1) We can talk about the angles being congruent, $\angle A \cong \angle D$.

2) We can talk about the measures of the angles being equal by writing m$\angle A$ = m$\angle D$ ("m" stands for "the measure of").

1. For each pair of corresponding parts (sides and angles) of the triangles above, write two statements to indicate the congruence.

2. Indicate that all pairs of corresponding parts (sides and angles) of the congruent shapes below are congruent in two different ways.

a)

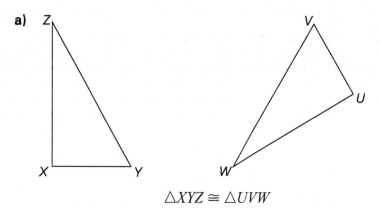

△*XYZ* ≅ △*UVW*

b)

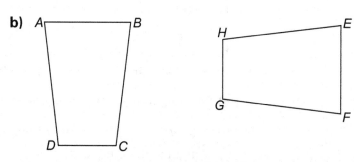

quadrilateral *ABCD* ≅ quadrilateral *EFGH*

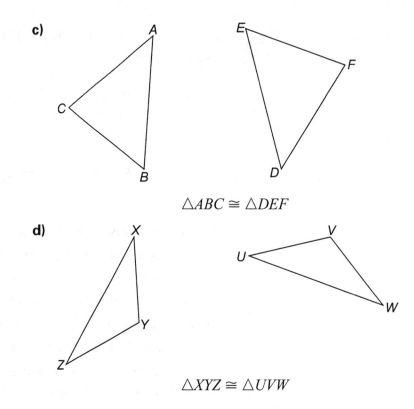

c)

$\triangle ABC \cong \triangle DEF$

d)

$\triangle XYZ \cong \triangle UVW$

In the examples above, you were given that the figures were congruent and you named the congruent corresponding parts.

What if you are trying to find out if two given triangles are congruent? What must you do in order to determine this? Let's investigate.

Investigation 1: Side-Side-Side Property

If three sides of one triangle are equal in measure to three sides of another triangle, will the triangles be congruent?

In other words, will the corresponding pairs of angles always be congruent?

3. Discuss with a partner how to use inductive reasoning to investigate this question. Make a prediction.

4. Use your AngLegs™. Working with a partner, make at least four pairs of triangles that have corresponding sides that are the same length. For example, you and your partner may construct a triangle with sides whose colors are red, purple, and yellow.

a) Are the triangles in each pair congruent? How do you know?

b) Can you form two triangles that have corresponding sides of equal length that are not congruent?

c) Make a generalization about triangles with corresponding sides that are the same length.

5. Your generalization is based on several examples. Do these examples prove that your generalization is true? Explain.

You have just discovered a triangle congruence property called the Side-Side-Side Property or SSS Property. This property states:

If three sides of one triangle are congruent to three sides of another triangle, then the two triangles are congruent.

We mark congruent sides with the same number of tick marks, as shown below. Using the SSS Property, you see that $\triangle ABC \cong \triangle DEF$.

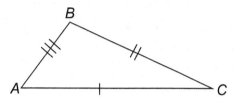

Investigation 2: Side-Angle-Side Property

If two sides of one triangle are equal in measure to two sides of another triangle, will the triangles be congruent?

6. Follow the same procedure as Investigation 1 and draw a conclusion.

  a) Make a prediction.

  b) With your Anglegs™, make at least 4 pairs of triangles that have two sides equal in measure. Are the triangles in each pair always congruent?

  c) Make a generalization.

7. When two sides of one triangle are equal in measure to two sides of another triangle, are the two triangles congruent? If not, what else do you need to know about the triangles? Discuss this with your partner.

 **Hint**
See page 154

You should have discovered another important property, the Side-Angle-Side Property or SAS Property. This property states:

If two sides and the included angle (the angle between these two sides) of one triangle are congruent to two sides and the included angle of another triangle, then the two triangles are congruent.

To show that two angles are congruent, we put the same number of tick marks on curves that mark the angles. For the two triangles below, we can use the SAS property to conclude that $\triangle XYZ \cong \triangle UVW$.

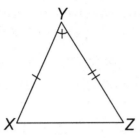 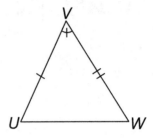

 NOTE It is important that the congruent corresponding angle be the included angle. The word *included* in front of *angle* is very important when stating the property.

8. Draw two triangles to show that if the two sides and a non-included angle of one triangle are congruent to two sides and a non-included angle of another, then the triangles may not be congruent. Share your drawing with a partner.

Investigation 3: Angle-Side-Angle Property

Suppose you only know that one pair of corresponding sides of two triangles is congruent. What would you have to know about the angles to conclude that the triangles are congruent?

9. Follow the same procedure as Investigation 1 and draw a conclusion.

   a) Make a prediction.

   b) With your Anglegs™, make at least 4 pairs of triangles that have one pair of sides equal in measure. Are the triangles always congruent? Are they ever congruent?

   c) Make a generalization.

You should have just discovered another important property. It is called the **Angle-Side-Angle Property** or **ASA Property**. This property states:

If two angles and the **included side** (the side between the two angles) of one triangle are congruent to two angles and the included side of another triangle, then the triangles are congruent.

10. Talk to your partner and answer the question posed below.

For the two triangles below, can we use the ASA Property to conclude that △MNO ≅ △RST?

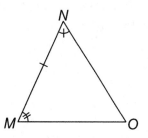
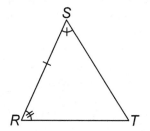

⬆W rap It Up

Troy said that, to be sure two triangles are congruent, you need to check that *all* the corresponding angles are congruent to each other and *all* the corresponding sides are the same length. Is he correct? Discuss this with your partner. Explain your reasoning.

MATHEMATICALLY SPEAKING

▸ acute triangle

▸ Angle-Side-Angle (ASA) Property

▸ corresponding angles

▸ corresponding sides

▸ equiangular triangle

▸ equilateral triangle

▸ included angle

▸ included side

▸ isosceles triangle

▸ obtuse triangle

▸ right triangle

▸ scalene triangle

▸ Side-Angle-Side (SAS) Property

▸ Side-Side-Side (SSS) Property

**Write About It**

1. **a)** Explain the SAS and ASA Properties in words and with a diagram.

   b) How do you use these properties to show that two triangles are congruent?

2. Define congruent triangles using the idea of corresponding sides and angles. Include a sketch of congruent triangles and name all corresponding sides and angles.

3. Which triangles are congruent? Explain your reasoning. You may use a ruler to help you.

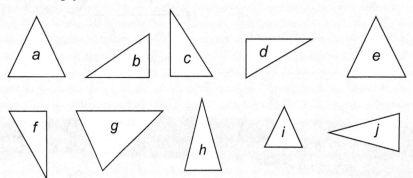

4. Without measuring, state whether or not the two triangles are congruent. If they are congruent, use either the SSS Property or the SAS Property to explain why.

   a)

   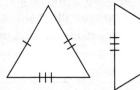

   c)

   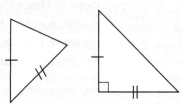

   b)

   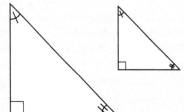

   d)

   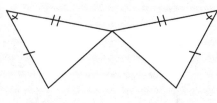

5. a) How might the SSS Property come in handy for an architect?

b) How might this property be used by construction workers?

Hint
See page 154

6. Here is a picture of the John Hancock Center in Chicago, Illinois. Are the triangles in each indicated pair congruent? Why or why not?

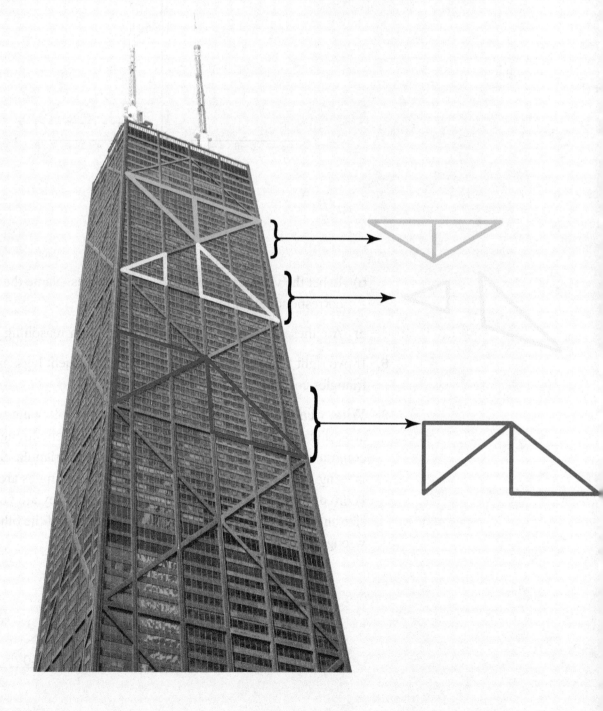

7. The right side of a roof with a triangular attic air vent is shown by a dashed line (- - - -) below.

a) The left side of this roof is a mirror image of the right. What are the coordinates of the five points of the vertices for the left side of the roof and the attic air vent?

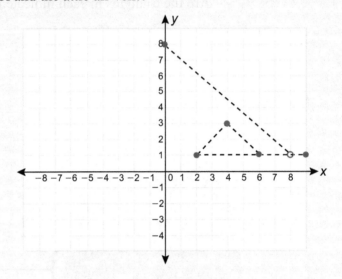

b) Label the vertices of the two small triangles. Name the corresponding parts of these two triangles.

c) Are these triangles congruent? Explain your reasoning.

8. If two right triangles have corresponding congruent legs, are the triangles congruent? Justify your answer.

9. **What went wrong?** Patrice told Pedro that the following two triangles are congruent because two sides and an angle of one triangle are congruent to two sides and an angle of the other triangle. She says she is using the SAS Property to conclude that the triangles are congruent. Pedro disagrees. "How can they be congruent? They are not the same size and shape and one will not fit exactly on top of the other." What is wrong with Patrice's reasoning?

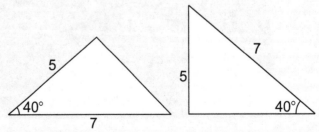

10. Is there an SSSS Property for quadrilaterals? In other words, if four sides of one quadrilateral are congruent to the corresponding four sides of another, are the quadrilaterals congruent? Use drawings to explain your answer.

Hint
See page 154

11. As a master carpenter, your job is to ensure that walls are properly braced so that they don't collapse. A frame is rigid when its sides cannot be tilted to the right or left, and corner angles always remain at 90°. Which of the following wall frames is the most rigid? Why?

Hint
See page 154

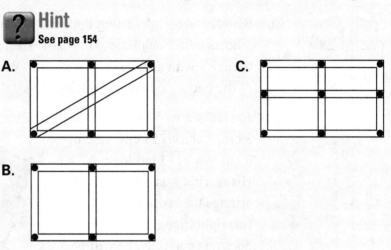

A.

C.

B.

12 Find five sets of congruent triangles in the architecture in your neighborhood. Only two of these structures can be houses. Sketch the structures, outline the congruent triangles and identify where the structure is located.

13. In parallelogram *ABCD*, explain why diagonal $\overline{AC}$ divides the parallelogram into two congruent triangles.

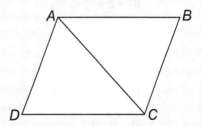

14. Explore other combinations of congruent angles and sides (other than SSS, SAS and ASA) to see if two triangles are congruent. Do any combinations always work (that is, are two triangles always congruent using a certain combination of angles and sides)? Explain your findings.

15. There are 80 students taking a 45-minute test. Twenty-five finish 10 minutes early, and 32 finish with 5 minutes left. The rest had to stop at 45 minutes. What was the average amount of time spent on the test?

16. Sam found an interesting button. It has a radius of 2 cm, and it has 3 holes in it. Each hole is the same size, and all three are right isosceles triangles with a leg length of 0.5 cm. What is the total area of the button, without the holes? Use 3.14 for π.

17. Jon has six wooden rods, which are 3 cm, 7 cm, $\sqrt{153}$ cm, 12 cm, 8 cm and $\sqrt{113}$ cm long. His teacher asked him to arrange the six rods into two right triangles. If he does this correctly, he will be the next caretaker of the class pet, the Grislaw beast. All his classmates are jealous! How does Jon separate the rods so that they form two right triangles?

18. If $x = {}^-4$, $y = 3$ and $z = {}^-6$, find the following values:

a) $x + y - z$

d) $x - \frac{y}{z}$

b) $xy + z$

e) $x - \frac{z}{y}$

c) xyz

f) $\frac{x - z}{y}$

19. Expressed as a decimal, 4% is

A. 0.04

C. 4.0

B. 0.4

D. 4

LESSON 2.2 Exploring Congruency Using Transformations

Start It Off

Which of the following pairs of figures appear to be exactly alike in shape and size? How did you determine this?

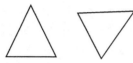
1.

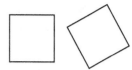
4.

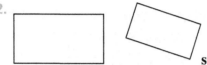
2.   s

5.

3.

6.

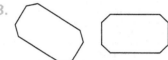

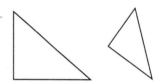

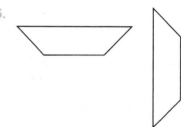

MATHEMATICALLY SPEAKING

▶ transformation

In the last lesson, you determined if two polygons were congruent by measuring corresponding sides and angles. You can also show two shapes are congruent by sliding, turning or flipping one to see if it fits exactly on top of the other. In this lesson, you will explore these moves, called transformations.

Transformations

MATHEMATICALLY SPEAKING

▶ image

▶ rigid transformation

When you move all points of a figure in a plane according to a common rule or operation, you create an image of the original figure. This process of moving is called a transformation. If the image is congruent to the original figure, the process is considered a rigid transformation.

MATHEMATICALLY SPEAKING

▶ translation
▶ rotation
▶ reflection
▶ reflection line (line of symmetry)

There are three types of rigid transformations.

- Translation: – A translation slides each point of a figure the same distance and same direction. Architects often use this when designing buildings. Notice how each of the windows in this building is an image of each other, just slid up or down, right or left.

- Rotation: A rotation turns each point of a figure in the same direction, by the same angle, around the same center of rotation. A turn angle is often used to show the center of rotation (at the vertex of the angle) as well as the direction (clockwise or counterclockwise) and the size (or number of degrees) of the rotation. How was rotational symmetry used in the design of this windmill? What is the center of rotation of the turn? What is the measure of the angle to move from one blade of the windmill to the next?

- Reflection: A reflection flips each point of a figure over a line, called the reflection line or line of symmetry. Many buildings are designed so that one side of the building is a reflection of the other. Can you find the line of symmetry in the Taj Mahal or the Parthenon?

You can use tracing paper to copy the original figure and then translate, rotate or reflect it to find its image under the given transformation. You can explore the same thing using a dynamic geometry program such as Geometer's Sketchpad®. You might also be able to do this by visualizing the results using a geoboard or grid or dot paper.

Example

Translation: To show how a figure is translated, a slide arrow is often used to indicate both the distance and the direction. Note that in this figure, the red slide arrow shows that the original pentagon is moved down and to the left. When the figure is drawn on dot paper such as this, you can simply count the number of spaces to move each vertex down and to the left to form the image. You may also trace the original

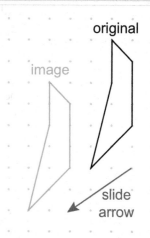

pentagon and the slide arrow onto a small sheet of tracing paper. Then move the tracing paper down and to the left so that the vertex of the traced arrow moves to the tip of the original arrow, along the line of the slide. This moves every point of the original pentagon in the same direction and distance as the slide arrow, forming the image.

Rotation: To show how a figure is rotated, a turn angle is often used to show the center of rotation (at the vertex of the angle), the direction (clockwise or counterclockwise) and the size (number of degrees) of the rotation. Note the red 180°-turn angle in this diagram. To find the image of the original quadrilateral, you can trace the original quadrilateral and the turn angle onto a small sheet of tracing paper, being careful to mark the vertex of the angle.

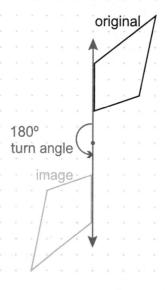

You can then rotate your tracing paper the given number of degrees by moving one ray of the angle to the other in the direction indicated, keeping the vertex in the same place. Turning the tracing paper in this fashion forms an image that is a 180°-counterclockwise rotation of the original quadrilateral about the center of the turn angle.

Reflection: To show how a figure is reflected, a reflection line, also known as a line of symmetry, is often drawn. To find the image of this quadrilateral, you can trace the original quadrilateral and the reflection line and any point on the reflection line onto a small piece of tracing paper. You can then flip the tracing paper over, matching the reflection line and its point to form the image.

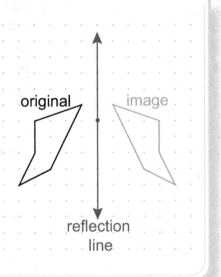

original   image

reflection line

For the following transformations, use a tool of your choice.

1. Copy each figure, and then draw the image using translations. Slide each figure in the direction and distance indicated by the red slide angle.

   a)

   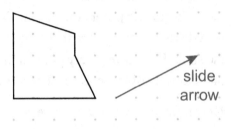

   slide arrow

   b)

   slide arrow

   c) Create your own translation question and trade with a partner to solve.

2. Copy each figure, and then draw the image using the indicated rotation.

   a) Use point A as the center of the rotation and turn the figure 90° counterclockwise to form the image.

   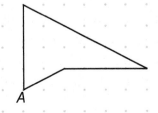

   A

b) Use point O as the center of rotation and turn the figure as shown to form the image.

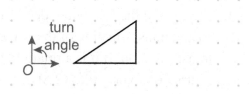

c) Create your own rotation question and trade with a partner to solve.

3. Copy each figure and then draw the image of the figure reflected over the line shown.

a)

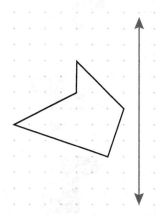

b)

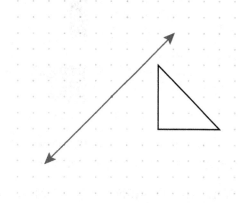

c) Create your own reflection question and trade with a partner to solve

4. For each of the following, determine if the black image represents a rigid transformation of the white figure. If so, list the type of transformation. If it is a rotation, list the type of turn: $\frac{1}{4}$-turn (90°), $\frac{1}{2}$-turn (180°) or $\frac{3}{4}$-turn (270°); clockwise or counterclockwise. Note that some may use a combination of transformations.

	Original Figure (white) Image (black)	Rigid Transformation? (yes or no)	Type of Transformation(s)
a)			
b)			
c)			
d)			
e)			

Each of the figures in the above table is a pentomino. Pentominoes are made up of five congruent squares, connected along their edges.

5. Work with a partner to find all of the possible pentominoes. Record each one on $\frac{3}{4}$-inch grid paper. How do you know if they are all different? Cut them out and color each one a different color. Use the same color to color both sides of each shape.

Hint
See page 154

6. You have this pentomino that you want to move to match the one on the grid below.

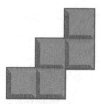

a) Would you have to flip or rotate the pentomino to make it fit? Is there more than one way you could do this?

b) Imagine that you flip or rotate the pentomino so its orientation matches the one in the grid. Now the pentomino sits just inside the upper left-hand corner of the grid. How many spaces to the right and how many spaces down would you have to move it to make it fit on the one on the grid?

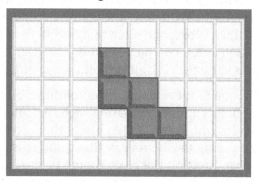

7. You have this grid with three pentominoes.

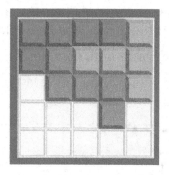

You want to fill the rest of the grid using different pentominoes. You have these nine pieces left.

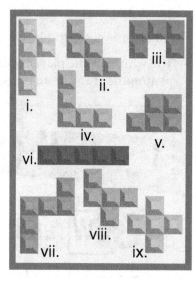

a) Which pentominoes might you use to fill the grid? Would you rotate or reflect the pieces to make them fit?

b) After each piece is in the correct orientation, imagine that it is just inside the upper left-hand corner of the grid. How many spaces to the right and how many down would you move each shape to fill the grid?

c) Can you find another way to fill the grid?

Place the Pentominoes

Players: Two players (or two teams of two players each)

Materials: One set of 12 pentominoes, one 8×8 playing grid

DIRECTIONS: Players take turns choosing a pentomino and placing it on the grid. The goal is to place the most pentominoes or be the last person to be able to place a piece on the grid.

- To begin the game, flip a coin to see who should choose first.

- The first player starts by picking a pentomino and telling the other player whether it should be left in its current orientation, reflected and/or rotated. After announcing the move, Player 1 places the piece just inside the upper left-hand corner of the playing grid using the moves described, and tells the second player how many spaces to the right and how many spaces down the piece should be moved. Player 1 then moves the piece that number of spaces. If the piece lands in the correct location and is completely inside the grid, Player 1 scores a point and the pentomino is left where it is. It is then the second player's turn.

- Player 2 chooses one of the remaining pentominoes and tells Player 1 whether it should be left in its current orientation, reflected and/or rotated to fit into an empty space on the grid. Player 2 then places the piece in the upper left-hand corner of the grid using the moves described, and tells the first player how many spaces and in what direction the piece should be moved. Player 2 then moves the piece. If the piece lands in the correct empty spaces, Player 2 scores a point, leaves the pentomino where it is, and it is Player 1's turn.

- If at any time, the piece lands on top of part of another pentomino, the player loses a turn and the pentomino is returned to the pile as a possible future choice.

- Play continues with players taking turns until no more moves are possible.

- The winner is the player with the most points, or the last player to place a pentomino if the score is tied.

 **rap It Up**

Discuss with a partner the three types of rigid transformations. Explain how you would find the image of a figure using each type of transformation and a tool of your choice.

MATHEMATICALLY SPEAKING

▶ image

▶ pentomino

▶ reflection

▶ reflection line (line of symmetry)

▶ rigid transformation

▶ rotation

▶ translation

▶ transformation

 **Write About It**

1. Describe three types of rigid transformations. How are they alike and how are they different? Give a real-world example of how each is used.

2. Copy each figure onto dot paper, and then draw the image using the indicated transformation.

   a) Reflect about line *l*

   b) Rotate 180° counterclockwise about point *P*

   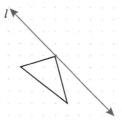

   c) Translate three spaces left and two spaces up

3. For each of the following, copy the figures and list each step in the transformation from the figure on the left to the image on the right.

   • For each translation, draw an arrow to show the distance and the direction.

   • For each rotation, put an X on the center of rotation and describe or draw an angle to show the size and direction of the turn.

   • For each reflection, draw the line of reflection. Note that some may use a combination of transformations. See if you can find more than one way to do each of these.

a)

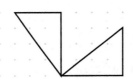

b)

c)

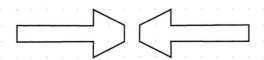

d)

e)

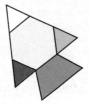

Think Beyond

f)

g)

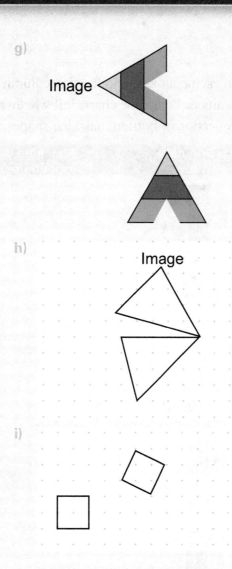

Image

h)

Image

i)

4. Match each pentomino in the first column with one or more of the pentominoes below the chart. Tell whether it would take a rotation or a reflection or both to make the shapes match.

Original Pentomino	Matching Pentomino(es)	Rotation and/or Reflection?

i.　　　　ii.　　　　iii.　　　　iv.　　　　v.

vi.　　　　vii.　　　　viii.　　　　ix.　　　　x.

xi.　　　　xii.

5. Choose three of the pentominoes and describe how you would translate them to show they are congruent to the pentominoes in this grid.

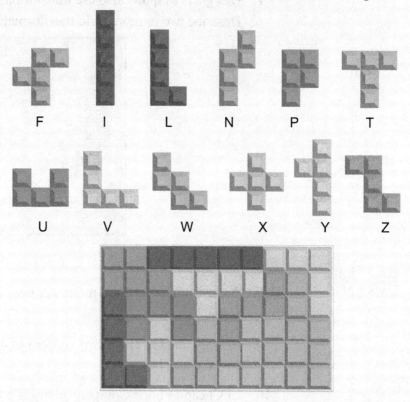

F I L N P T

U V W X Y Z

6. At Accent on Architecture ![Accent on Architecture logo], architects were involved in the design of the two structures below. Describe two or more types of rigid transformations that they used, in each design.

a)

b)

7. Designers of quilts also use transformations to create their designs. Describe two or more rigid transformations the designer of this quilt used.

Think Back

8. A car is traveling at 55 miles per hour. How many feet per second is that?

9. If (0, 0) and (1, 2) are two vertices of a square, what might the other two vertices be?

10. El Cheapo Phone Company charges a yearly fee of $45 plus $0.05 per minute. Talkalot Phone Company charges $0.14 per minute but no yearly fee. Which company offers the better deal? How many minutes in a year would you have to talk for the companies to charge you the same amount?

11. Find the principal square root of each number. Do not use a calculator. Write an equation for each (for example, $\sqrt{81} = 9$).

   a) 121

   b) 0.49

   c) 0.0081

   d) $\frac{49}{144}$

   e) 1.44

12. The measure of two angles of an isosceles triangle are 40°. Bo says that this is an acute triangle since both angles measure less than 90°. Do you agree? Why or why not?

Transformations on a Coordinate Plane

➡ **Start It Off**

1. Copy the Cartesian coordinate grid and then plot and label each of the following points. Connect the points in order with line segments, and then connect the first and last points.

$A\,(-2, 3)$ $\qquad$ $B\,(6, 3)$ $\qquad$ $C\,(8, -2)$ $\qquad$ $D\,(0, -2)$

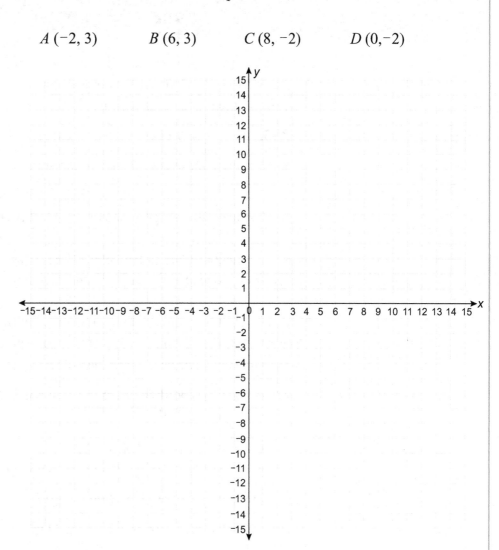

2. What shape is this?

3. Choose a polygon of your own and write directions using vertex coordinates so someone else can duplicate it.

In 1637, René Descartes designed the Cartesian coordinate system as a visual way to combine algebra and geometry. In the Cartesian coordinate system, points in the plane are named using an ordered pair of numbers, (x, y). Recall that the first number (the x-coordinate) tells us how many units to the right or left the point is from the vertical axis, and the second number (the y-coordinate) tells us how many units the point is above or below the horizontal axis.

Polygon Translations

1. Plot and label each of the following points on the same grid you used in the Start It Off. Connect the points in order with line segments, and then connect the first and last points.

   $A'(3, 3)$ $B'(11, 3)$ $C'(13, -2)$ $D'(5, -2)$

   a) Compare these coordinates to those in Start It Off. What do you notice?

   b) Compare this shape to the one in Start It Off. What do you notice?

    ' is read as *prime* and therefore A' is read as *A prime*.
   Also, " is read as *double prime* and ''' is read as *triple prime*.

2. Again, start by graphing the points given in Start It Off: $A(-2, 3)$, $B(6, 3)$, $C(8, -2)$ and $D(0, -2)$. For each point, leave the x-coordinate the same and subtract 3 from the y-coordinate.

   a) Record the coordinates for the new points and label them A'', B'', C'' and D''.

   b) Plot these points on the same grid. Connect the new points in order with line segments and then connect the first and last points.

   c) Compare this new shapes on the grid. What do you notice?

   d) Compare this shape to the one in Question 1. What do you notice?

3. Again, start with the points $A(-2, 3)$, $B(6, 3)$, $C(8, -2)$ and $D(0, -2)$. Subtract 2 from each x-coordinate and add 4 to each y-coordinate. Label these A''', B''', C''' and D'''.

   a) Predict what will happen when you plot these points.

   b) Plot the points on the same grid you used for Question 2 and check your predictions.

4. Plot a polygon of your choice on a coordinate grid and record the points for the vertices.

a) Choose any number to add to each of the x-coordinates and keep the y-coordinates the same. Predict what will happen when you plot these new points. Plot the points to check your prediction.

b) Choose a number to add to the y-coordinates, while keeping the x-coordinates the same. Predict what will happen when you plot those new points. Plot the points to check your prediction.

c) Compare your polygons with a partner. What generalizations can you make?

5. In the last lesson, you explored translations without using a coordinate plane and found that a translated figure is congruent to the original. Is that also true for translated figures on the coordinate plane? How do you know?

Polygon Reflections

In the last lesson, you explored reflecting a figure over a line using dot paper and other tools. Here you are going to explore what happens when you plot a figure on a coordinate plane and then reflect it.

6. Plot a quadrilateral in the first quadrant of a four-quadrant coordinate plane. Label the vertices A, B, C and D and list the coordinates of each.

a) Predict what the coordinates of the vertices will be when you reflect the quadrilateral over the x-axis. Plot the reflected quadrilateral and label its vertices A', B', C' and D'. List the coordinates of each vertex. Do the coordinates match your prediction? Compare your results with a partner.

b) Predict what the coordinates of the vertices will be when you reflect the original quadrilateral over the y-axis. Plot the reflected quadrilateral and label its vertices A", B", C" and D". List the coordinates of each vertex. Do the coordinates match your prediction? Compare your results with a partner.

c) For each of your three quadrilaterals, find the length and slope of each line segment. Are all three quadrilaterals congruent? How do you know?

7. Plot a pentagon in at least three quadrants of a four-quadrant coordinate plane. Label the vertices E, F, G, H and J and list the coordinates of each.

   a) Predict what the coordinates of the vertices will be when you reflect the pentagon over the x-axis. Plot the reflected pentagon and label its vertices E', F', G', H' and J'. List the coordinates of each vertex. Do the coordinates match your prediction? Compare your results with a partner.

   b) Predict what the coordinates of the vertices will be when you reflect the original pentagon over the y-axis. Plot the reflected pentagon and label its vertices E'', F'', G'', H'' and J''. List the coordinates of each vertex. Do the coordinates match your prediction? Compare your results with a partner.

   c) Can you make a generalization about congruence when reflecting a figure over the x- or y-axis? Explain why your generalization would hold for all types of figures.

Polygon Rotations

As you know, the third type of rigid transformation is a turn or rotation.

8. Plot a quadrilateral in the first quadrant of a four-quadrant coordinate plane. Label the vertices W, X, Y and Z and list the coordinates of each.

   a) Predict what the coordinates of the vertices will be when you rotate the quadrilateral 90° counterclockwise around the origin. Plot the rotated quadrilateral and label its vertices W', X', Y' and Z'. List the coordinates of each vertex. Do the coordinates match your prediction? Compare your results with a partner.

   b) Predict what the coordinates of the vertices will be when you rotate the original quadrilateral 180° counterclockwise around the origin. Plot the rotated quadrilateral and label its vertices W'', X'', Y'' and Z''. List the coordinates of each vertex. Do the coordinates match your prediction? Compare your results with a partner.

   c) For each of your three quadrilaterals, find the length and slope of each line segment. Are all three quadrilaterals congruent? How do you know?

   d) Make a generalization about the coordinates of the image of any polygon that is rotated 90° or 180° counterclockwise about the origin for any polygon with vertices in the first quadrant. Give reasons to support your generalization.

   e) Make a generalization about the size and shape of the image of any polygon that is rotated 90° or 180° counterclockwise about the origin for any polygon with vertices in the first quadrant. Give reasons to support your generalization.

 **Think Beyond**

9. Plot a triangle so that its vertices are in three quadrants of a four-quadrant coordinate plane. Label the vertices *K*, *L* and *M* and list the coordinates of each.

a) Predict what the coordinates of the vertices will be when you rotate the triangle 90° clockwise around the origin. Plot the rotated triangle and label its vertices *K′*, *L′* and *M′*. List the coordinates of each vertex. Do the coordinates match your prediction? Compare your results with a partner.

b) Predict what the coordinates of the vertices will be when you rotate the original triangle 180° clockwise around the origin. Plot the rotated triangle and label its vertices *K″*, *L″* and *M″*. List the coordinates of each vertex. Do the coordinates match your prediction? Compare your results with a partner.

c) For each of your three triangles, find the length and slope of each line segment. Are all three triangles congruent? How do you know?

d) Make a generalization about the coordinates of the image of any polygon that is rotated 90° or 180° clockwise about the origin for any polygon. Give reasons to support your generalization.

e) Make a generalization about the size and shape of the image of any polygon that is rotated 90° or 180° clockwise about the origin for any polygon. Give reasons to support your generalization.

Putting It All Together

10. Plot a triangle so that it lies in the first quadrant of a four-quadrant coordinate plane. Label the vertices *P*, *Q* and *R* and list the coordinates of each.

a) Rotate the triangle *PQR* 90° counterclockwise around the origin. Label the vertices of the image *P′*, *Q′* and *R′* and list the coordinates of each.

b) Reflect the triangle *P′Q′R′* over the *x*-axis. Label the vertices of the image *P″*, *Q″* and *R″* and list the coordinates of each.

c) Translate the triangle *P″Q″R″* three spaces to the right and four spaces up. Label the vertices of the image *P‴*, *Q‴* and *R‴* and list the coordinates of each.

d) Describe a sequence of translations that would move triangle *P‴Q‴R‴* back to triangle *PQR*. Compare these translations to the series of translations that move triangle *PQR* to triangle *P‴Q‴R‴*.

11. Plot a triangle on a four-quadrant coordinate plane and list the coordinates of each vertex.

a) Describe a series of transformations that would plot an image of the triangle so the image and the original triangle together form a parallelogram.

b) Can you find more than one way to do this?

c) Compare your results with a partner. Did you start with the same type of triangle? Did you use the same series of transformations?

GAME · · · · · **Transformation Challenge** · · · · ·

Players: Two players (or two teams of two players each)

Materials: grid paper and rulers

DIRECTIONS:

- Each player plots a polygon on a coordinate grid and labels the vertices.

- Without showing the other player, each player then creates a series of two images using any combination of transformations, and carefully records the steps. For example, a player might first plot a triangle and label the vertices A, B and C. The player might then reflect the triangle over the y-axis and label the vertices of the image A', B' and C'. The next step might be to rotate triangle $A'B'C'$ 60° counterclockwise around the origin to create a new image labeled $A''B''C''$.

- Each player then copies the original polygon and the final image onto a new coordinate grid and labels each.

- Partners then exchange grids and challenge each other to find a series of transformations that starts with the final image and moves it onto the original polygon.

- When finished, partners check each other's transformations. Players receive a point for a correct series of transformations. If two or more different series of transformations are given for the same pair of polygons, the player receives two points for the second series, three points for the third series, and this pattern continues with each additional transformation series worth one more point than the previous one.

-  Use more than two transformations, including at least one rotation.

 **Wrap It Up**

You have a quadrilateral whose vertex coordinates are A (6, 7), B (1, 7), C (1, 5) and D (6, 5).

- You translate the quadrilateral 3 units to the left and 6 units down.
  What are the coordinates of the new vertices? List these for A', B', C' and D'.

- Plot quadrilaterals ABCD and A'B'C'D' on the same coordinate grid.

- Compare the quadrilaterals' shapes, sizes and locations.

Write
About It

1. You have a triangle with the coordinates A (6, 5), B (5, 7) and C (2, 5).

   a) Translate the triangle 3 units to the left and 6 units down. What are the new coordinates of the vertices? List these as A', B' and C'.

   b) Rotate triangle ABC 90° counterclockwise about the origin. What are the new coordinates of the vertices? Label these A'', B'' and C''.

   c) Reflect triangles ABC over the x-axis. What are the new coordinates of the vertices? Label these A''', B''' and C'''.

   d) Plot triangles ABC, $A'B'C'$, $A''B''C''$ and $A'''B'''C'''$ on the same coordinate grid.

   e) Compare the triangles' shapes, sizes and locations.

2. Plot the pentagon with the following vertices on a coordinate grid:
   A (4, 7), B (2, 8), C (5, 1), D (6, 4) and E (5, 9).

   a) If this pentagon is translated 3 units to the right and 1 unit down, what will be the new coordinates of the vertices? List these as A', B', C', D' and E'.

   b) Rotate pentagon $ABCDE$ 180° counterclockwise about the origin. What are the new coordinates of the vertices? Label these A'', B'', C'', D'' and E''.

   c) Reflect pentagon $ABCDE$ over the y-axis. What are the new coordinates of the vertices? Label these A''', B''', C''', D''' and E'''.

   d) Plot and label all three new pentagons on the same coordinate grid.

   e) Compare the pentagons' shapes, sizes and locations. Does the type of polygon affect the images created by different types of transformations?

3. A quadrilateral has vertices at A' (2, 9), B' (3, 7), C' (4, 6) and D' (5, 8). This quadrilateral is a translation of a quadrilateral $ABCD$ by 2 units left and 2 units down. What are the coordinates of the vertices of quadrilateral $ABCD$?

4. Copy the following grid onto your own grid paper and plot a triangle with vertices at $A\,(-4, 3)$, $B\,(5, -1)$ and $C\,(3, 4)$.

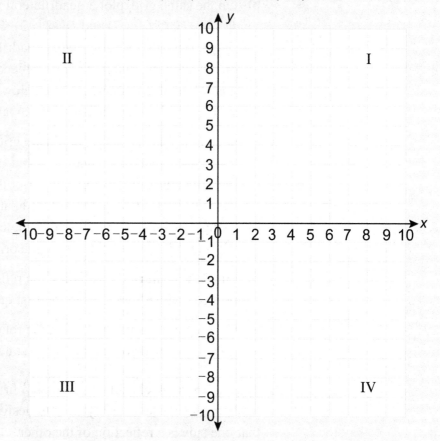

a) Reflect the triangle over the x-axis. List the vertices A', B' and C'. Plot the triangle image on the same Cartesian grid.

b) Compare the triangles' shapes, sizes, and locations.

c) How does reflecting a figure with vertices in three quadrants compare to reflecting a figure with all vertices in the first quadrant?

5. On another four-quadrant grid, plot a quadrilateral with vertices at $A\,(5, 3)$, $B\,(5, 7)$, $C\,(4, 7)$ and $D\,(2, 3)$.

a) On the same grid, plot a quadrilateral with vertices at $A'\,(-5, 3)$, $B'\,(-5, 7)$, $C'\,(-4, 7)$ and $D'\,(-2, 3)$. Compare the vertices, shape, size, and location of this quadrilateral to your original one. Is the new quadrilateral a transformation of the original? If so, what type of transformation?

b) On the same grid, plot a quadrilateral with vertices at A'' (5, −3), B'' (5, −7), C'' (4, −7) and D'' (2, −3). Compare the vertices, shape, size and location of this quadrilateral to your original one. Is quadrilateral $A''B''C''D''$ a reflection of either of the other quadrilaterals? If so, which one? How do the coordinates of the vertices of these quadrilaterals compare?

c) On a new four-quadrant coordinate grid, plot a triangle of your choosing. Label the vertices A, B and C and list the coordinates of each vertex. Plot its reflection over the x-axis and label the new triangle $A'B'C'$. Compare the coordinates of the vertices of the new triangle to those of the original triangle. Repeat these steps to plot triangle $A''B''C''$, the reflection of the original triangle over the y-axis.

d) Give a general rule for finding the reflection over the x-axis of any polygon with all vertices in the first quadrant.

e) Give a general rule for finding the reflection over the y-axis of any polygon with all vertices in the first quadrant.

6. The Accent on Architecture firm has been hired to create a mathematics museum. They want to design the front of the building so that one side is a reflection of the other.

a) In the first quadrant of a four-quadrant coordinate grid, sketch a design that you might use for the right side of the front of the building. Include at least three different polygons and list their coordinates.

b) Reflect your figures from Part a, using the y-axis as your reflection line. List the coordinates of the reflected polygons.

c) Are the polygons on the left side congruent to the polygons on the right side? Explain.

7. Use the rectangle and its image for the following questions.

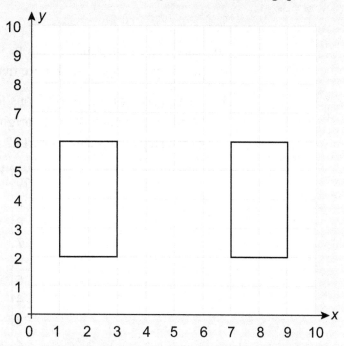

a) Describe a translation that would move the rectangle on the left onto the rectangle on the right.

b) Describe a reflection that would move the rectangle on the right onto the rectangle on the left.

c) Is there a rotation that would move the rectangle on the left onto the rectangle on the right? If so, give the center, size and direction of rotation. If not, explain why not.

d) Describe a series of transformations that would move the rectangle on the left onto the rectangle on the right. Include a rotation in the series.

8. Plot a triangle on a coordinate grid with vertices in three different quadrants. List the coordinates.

a) Describe a transformation that would form an image of the original triangle so the triangle and its image together form a larger triangle. Plot the image on the same grid and list its coordinates.

b) Is the image of the triangle congruent to the original? Explain how you know.

Think
Beyond

9. **a)** List a series of transformations to move quadrilateral *ABCD* onto its image. Can you find more than one way to do this?

b) List a series of transformations to move the image of the quadrilateral back onto the original. How does this compare to the steps you listed in Part a?

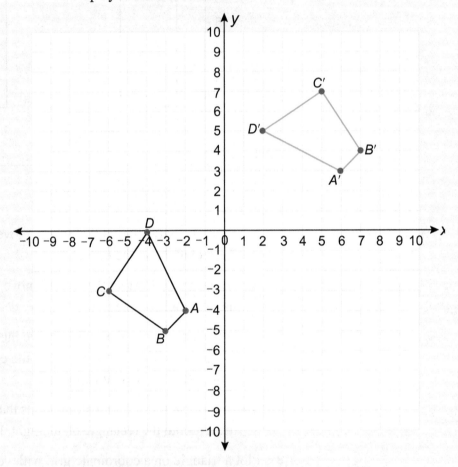

10. Complete the chart below for regular polygons. Remember that all sides are congruent in any regular polygon. The first row is done for you.

Number of Sides	Length of One Side	Name	Perimeter
3	2.5 cm	equilateral triangle	7.5 cm
		square	16 m
5			10 ft.
6	$\frac{1}{4}$ in.		
	3 m	regular octagon	
10			123 cm

11. Sadaf said that if you square her number, add 6 and multiply the result by 4, you will get 60. Write an equation to find her original number.

12. List a set of 5 numbers that have a mean of 21 and a median of 16.

13. a) Sketch an isosceles right triangle with a leg length of 3 cm.

    b) What is the area of your triangle?

    c) What is the perimeter of the triangle?

14. a) If the triangle in Question 13 is the base of a triangular prism with a height of 4.6 cm, what is the volume of the triangular prism?

    b) If the triangle in Question 13 is the base of a triangular pyramid with a height of 4.6 cm, what is the volume of the triangular pyramid?

Exploring Properties of Similar Triangles

Start It Off

For social studies class, Luke is making a poster-sized version of a credit card. He measures a credit card and finds that it is 5.5 cm wide and 8.5 cm long. He plans to make his poster 17 in. long.

1. What should the scale be for Luke's poster?

2. Do you have to know the centimeter-to-inch conversion to find the scale?

3. Given this scale, how wide will Luke's poster be?

A Closer Look at Corresponding Angles

You know that two triangles are congruent when the second one can be obtained from the first one by one or more translations, rotations and/or reflections. That means that the following corresponding parts are congruent:

- three sides (SSS)

- two sides and an included angle (SAS)

- two angles and an included side (ASA)

- two angles and a non-included side (AAS)

Let's take a further look at angles in triangles.

If we know that the three angles in one triangle are congruent to the three angles in another triangle, can the two triangles be congruent? Must they be congruent?

1. **a)** Can you find an example of two congruent triangles in which the three angles of one are congruent to the three angles in the other? Use your AngLegs™ to help you. If this is possible, draw a sketch and label the sides and angle measures.

b) Can you find an example of two noncongruent triangles in which the three angles of one are congruent to the three angles in the other? If this is possible, draw a sketch and label the sides and angle measures.

c) Draw a conclusion about whether or not two triangles can be or must be congruent if their corresponding angles are congruent.

2. Heraldo decided that if three angles of one triangle are congruent to the three angles of another triangle, the triangles are not necessarily congruent.

a) What does he mean?

b) Do you agree or disagree? State your reasoning.

MATHEMATICALLY SPEAKING

▶ similar figures

▶ similar triangles

▶ Angle-Angle-Angle (AAA) Similarity Property

Let's Review

You learned in earlier grades that similar figures have the same shape but not necessarily the same size. For example, the two rectangles below are similar. Notice that the corresponding angles in the rectangles are congruent.

We call two triangles in which three angles of one are congruent to three angles of the other similar triangles. In fact, there is a special property that states this.

> The Angle-Angle-Angle (or AAA) Similarity Property states that if three angles of one triangle are congruent to the three angles of another triangle, then the triangles are similar.

Something Special About the Sides

Sometimes the corresponding side lengths of similar triangles are congruent and sometimes they are not. In either case, there is something special about how they relate to one another.

In each of the following triangle pairs, the three angles of one triangle are congruent to the three angles of the other triangle. Their side lengths are shown in inches. We can set up a correspondence between pairs of congruent angles for each pair of triangles.

3. Using the correspondence relationships listed, name the corresponding sides in each pair.

a)

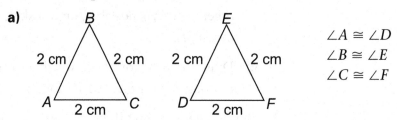

$\angle A \cong \angle D$
$\angle B \cong \angle E$
$\angle C \cong \angle F$

b)

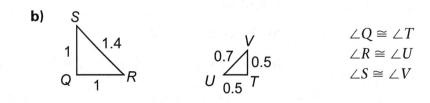

$\angle Q \cong \angle T$
$\angle R \cong \angle U$
$\angle S \cong \angle V$

c)

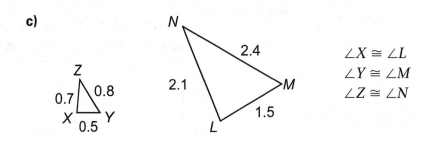

$\angle X \cong \angle L$
$\angle Y \cong \angle M$
$\angle Z \cong \angle N$

Let's Review

You have already learned about ratios and proportions. A ratio is the relationship between two numbers or quantities. A ratio of 1 to 4 can be rewritten as $1:4$, $\frac{1}{4}$ or as a single value, 0.25. A proportion is an equation that states that two ratios are equal, such as $\frac{1}{4} = \frac{2}{8}$.

---

4. a) Find the ratio of the lengths of each pair of corresponding sides for the triangle pairs in Question 3.

b) What do you notice?

You can write proportions to show the relationships among side lengths of similar triangles. One way to set up proportions for the corresponding sides of similar triangles is to write the lengths of the corresponding sides as a ratio. You can write the sides of the same triangle directly across from each other on opposite sides of the equation. For example, in Question 3b above, a proportion that shows that the ratios of two pairs of corresponding side lengths are equal is:

$$\frac{SQ}{VT} = \frac{SR}{VU}$$

5. a) Write a proportion comparing two different pairs of corresponding sides for the triangles in Question 3b.

b) Write a proportion comparing two pairs of corresponding sides for the triangles in Question 3a.

c) Write a proportion comparing two pairs of corresponding sides for the triangles in Question 3c.

d) Use your observations to predict the relationship between the ratios of corresponding sides of two triangles that have congruent corresponding angles.

6. Working in groups of four, test your prediction.

a) Each person should create a triangle with angle measures as follows: $m\angle A = 30°$, $m\angle B = 60°$ and $m\angle C = 90°$. Share your sketches and make sure that no two triangles are congruent.

b) Fill in the table below with your group. Write the lengths as decimals rounded to the nearest tenth of a cm.

Triangle	Length of $\overline{AB}$ in cm	Length of $\overline{BC}$ in cm	Length of $\overline{AC}$ in cm
1			
2			
3			
4			

c) Set up proportions between the lengths of the corresponding sides of the four triangles to see if the ratios are equal.

d) Share your findings with the class.

7. a) Make a generalization about ratios of corresponding sides of triangles with congruent corresponding angles. Was the prediction you made in 5d correct?"

b) What type of reasoning did you use to make your generalization? Explain.

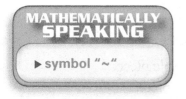

▶ symbol "~"

The symbol ~ means "is similar to." In Question 3, we can say $\triangle ABC \sim \triangle DEF$. We can also say $\triangle QRS \sim \triangle TUV$, and $\triangle XYZ \sim \triangle LMN$.

 We name pairs of similar triangles by listing their vertices in the order of their corresponding congruent angles.

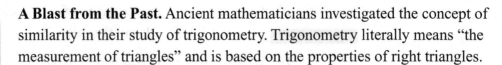

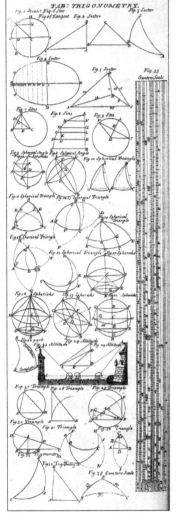

MATHEMATICALLY
SPEAKING

▶ Angle-Angle (AA)
  Similarity Theorem

▶ similar triangles

▶ trigonometry

A Blast from the Past. Ancient mathematicians investigated the concept of similarity in their study of trigonometry. Trigonometry literally means "the measurement of triangles" and is based on the properties of right triangles.

Mathematicians have discovered the relationships of similar triangles to be true for any angle measures! So we can state:

Similar triangles have congruent corresponding angles and corresponding sides are in proportion.

8. Melanie told Melik that you don't have to know that all three pairs of angles are congruent to show that two triangles are similar. She said all you need to know is that two pairs are congruent. She called this the Angle-Angle (AA) Similarity Theorem. Explain why Melanie's statement is true.

9. Each of the angles in the two triangles below measures 60°. Ana stated that these two triangles are similar. Jordan said they are congruent. Who is correct? Discuss with your partner.

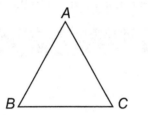
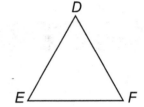

10. We have shown that if two triangles have corresponding angles congruent, then their corresponding sides are in proportion. Let's investigate the converse of this statement.

    If the corresponding sides of two triangles are in proportion, are their corresponding angles congruent?

    a) Create the following triangles with AngLegs™. Show that their sides are in proportion. Round the length of each side to the nearest hundredth of a centimeter.

    Measure each pair of corresponding angles.

    Triangle 1—use red, purple and blue pieces.
    Triangle 2—use orange, green and yellow pieces.

    Triangle 1— use 2 orange pieces and 1 purple piece.
    Triangle 2— use 2 green pieces and 1 blue piece.

    b) Find a different set of two triangles whose sides are in proportion. Measure their angles.

    c) Using AngLegs™, can you construct two triangles whose sides are in proportion but that are *not* similar? Explain.

11. Make a generalization about whether triangles are similar if their corresponding sides are in proportion.

 **W|rap It Up**

Leon said that similar triangles have exactly the same shape, but their sizes may not be the same. Do you agree? Compare this to the more formal definition of *similar triangles* on page 75.

MATHEMATICALLY SPEAKING

▶ Angle-Angle-Angle (AAA) Similarity Property

▶ Angle-Angle (AA) Similarity Theorem

▶ proportion

▶ ratio

▶ similar figures

▶ similar triangles

▶ symbol "~"

▶ trigonometry

 **Write About It**

1. Explain the AAA Similarity Property with words and pictures.

2. Match each mathematical symbol with its meaning.

   a) $\geq$ **i)** is perpendicular to

   b) $\leq$ **ii)** is similar to

   c) $\sim$ **iii)** is greater than or equal to

   d) $\cong$ **iv)** is congruent to

   e) $\perp$ **v)** is parallel to

   f) $\parallel$ **vi)** is less than or equal to

3. Prove the AA Triangle Similarity Theorem.

4. Below are the triangles from Question 3a in the lesson. Recall that these triangles are congruent. The ratio of their sides is $1:1$. Will this always be true for congruent triangles? Explain.

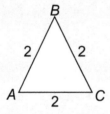

5. In the examples below, write whether or not the two triangles are similar based on the measurements given. If they are similar, state the ratio of the sides in simplest terms. If they are not similar, tell why not.

   a)

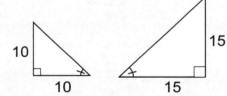

   b)

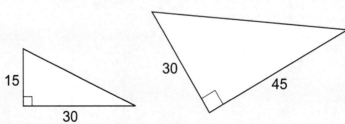

6. Fill in the blank with *always, sometimes* or *never*. If the answer is *sometimes*, give an example of when the statement is true and an example of when it is not true.

a) If two triangles are similar, their corresponding angles are _____ congruent.

b) If two triangles are similar, their corresponding sides are _____ in proportion.

c) If the corresponding angles of two triangles are congruent, the triangles are _____ congruent.

d) If the corresponding angles of two triangles are congruent, the triangles are _____ similar.

e) If the ratios of corresponding sides of two triangles are equal, then the two triangles are _____ similar.

f) If **two** angles of one triangle are congruent to two angles of another triangle, the triangles are _____ congruent.

g) If **two** angles of one triangle are congruent to two angles of another triangle, the triangles are _____ similar.

7. Fill in the blank with *always, sometimes* or *never*. Explain your reasoning.

a) Congruent triangles are _____ similar triangles.

b) Similar triangles are _____ congruent triangles.

8. There are three triangles in this drawing.

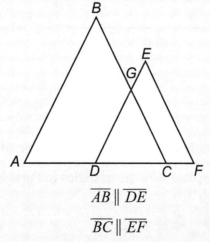

$$\overline{AB} \parallel \overline{DE}$$
$$\overline{BC} \parallel \overline{EF}$$

a) Name two similar triangles.

b) How do you know?

9. If four angles of one quadrilateral are congruent to the corresponding four angles of another quadrilateral, are the two quadrilaterals *sometimes, always* or *never* similar? Explain your answer. Use diagrams to illustrate.

10. Sammy wanted to make the definitions of *congruent triangles* and *similar triangles* easier to understand. He told his younger brother Sandy that congruent triangles have the same shape and size. He told him that similar triangles have the same shape but are different sizes. Were his definitions correct? Explain your answer.

11. In the similar triangles below, find the length represented by the variable.

a)

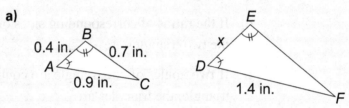

b)

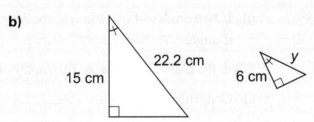

c)

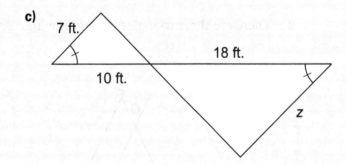

d) Find the lengths of the third side of each triangle in Parts a, b, and c.

e) Explain why the triangles in Parts b and c are similar.

12. Skyler tells Sophia he knows a way to make similar triangles that always works. He draws an X with both sides of the X being the same length, so that the line segments that connect the top points to each other and the bottom points to each other are parallel. He has drawn two of these figures below. Is he correct? Will the triangles in such a figure always be similar? Explain your thinking.

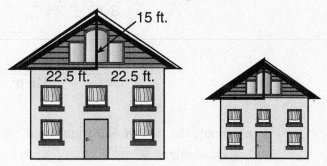

13. As an architect at 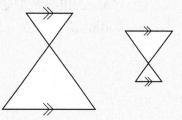, you have clients who want a studio placed next to their house. They want the studio to be similar to the house. You decide that the height of the studio roof should be $\frac{2}{3}$ the height of the roof of the house. See the diagram below.

15 ft.

22.5 ft.   22.5 ft.

Because the angles must remain the same, you know these are similar triangles. Use the given dimensions of the house's triangular roofline to find the dimensions of the new studio's roofline.

Career Connection: Check out this website to find out just what landscape architects do. www.thefutureschannel.com/dockets/hands-on_math/landscape_architects/

14. You can calculate distances across rivers, ponds and lakes using indirect measurement. Surveyors do this as part of their job.

To find the distance across the lake pictured below, surveyors will sight or plant an object such as a pole, marked A, on one side of the lake. On the opposite side of the lake, they line up points B and C so A, B and C are collinear. They also line up points D and E, so A, D and E are collinear, with $\overline{BD} \perp \overline{AC}$ and $\overline{CE} \perp \overline{AC}$.

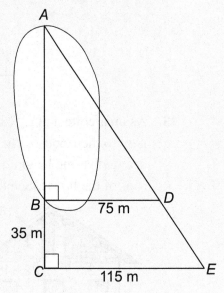

a) Name the two similar triangles in the diagram and explain why they are similar.

b) Write a proportion that compares a side length of the small triangle to the corresponding side length of the large triangle.

c) What is the distance across the lake? Explain how you got your answer.

15. Find the length of the missing side, x. Explain how you found your answer.

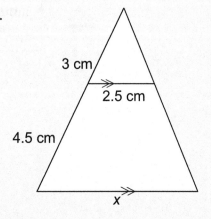

16. What values of x in the following equations make the y-value negative?

   a) $y = 2x - 7$

   b) $y = -3x + 12$

   c) $y = 4x - 142$

   d) $y = 0.5x - 11$

17. Shown below is an isosceles right triangle inscribed within a circle. The hypotenuse of the triangle is a diameter of the circle. What is the area of the shaded region?

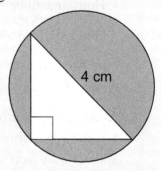

4 cm

18. A 17-foot ladder is leaning against a garage so that its base is 8 feet from the bottom of the garage and its top touches the bottom of the garage's roof. Which of the following equations would you use to find the height of the garage without the roof?

   A. $17^2 + 8^2 = x$

   B. $\sqrt{17^2 + 8^2} = x$

   C. $17^2 - 8^2 = x$

   D. $\sqrt{17^2 - 8^2} = x$

17 ft.

←8 ft.→

19. Samantha won a $1,000 scholarship to a seven-day tennis camp.

   - She has a choice for round-trip transportation of $315 by air or $185 by train.

   - She can have private lessons at the rate of $80 per day or group lessons for $50 per day.

   - Housing will be in local college dorms and is provided free of charge.

   - Food will cost $45 per day for the seven days.

   Find two ways she could plan her trip using only the scholarship money. Explain your reasoning clearly!

20. At the Long Acre Ranch, Mimi the pony is tied to a stake by an 8-meter rope. Mimi can run in any direction as far as the rope will allow. How much total area can Mimi cover?

Exploring Similarity Using Transformations

 **Start It Off**

What you found for similar triangles is true for all similar polygons: all corresponding angles are congruent and all corresponding sides are proportional. You can use pattern blocks to form shapes similar to the original.

1. Copy and complete the chart for each shape.

	Original Shape	Similar Shape: Each side twice as long as original	Similar Shape: Each side three times as long as original
a)	square		
b)	triangle		
c)	rhombus		
d)	trapezoid		

2. Check each of your shapes. Are the angles of each similar shape congruent to the corresponding angles in the original shape?

3. How does the perimeter of each shape compare to the perimeter of the original?

4. Give a general formula for the perimeter of any polygon that is similar to the original, if each side has a length that is n times the original.

5. How does the area of each shape compare to the area of the original?

6. Give a general formula for the area of any polygon that is similar to the original, if each side has a length that is n times the original.

Dilations

MATHEMATICALLY SPEAKING

▶ dilation

Have you noticed that when you click on a figure in a Microsoft® Word document, you can create a similar figure by dragging one of the corners? If the new figure is larger than the original, it is called an *enlargement*. If it is smaller than the original, it is called a *reduction*. Both enlargements and reductions are dilations of the original.

Note that if you drag a side of a figure instead of a corner, the new figure is not similar to the original. Why not?

You know that you can determine if two shapes are similar by measuring whether all angles are congruent and all side lengths are proportional. In this lesson, you will find another way to show that shapes are similar.

Nesting Figures

On triangular grid paper, draw the rhombuses that you found in the Start It Off (Question 1c). First, trace around the rhombus with each side three times the length of the original. Inside this rhombus and sharing a corresponding angle, draw an outline of the rhombus with sides twice as long as the original. Finally, outline the original rhombus so it shares the same corresponding angle with the other two. Draw a diagonal from the vertex that they all share to the opposite vertex of the largest rhombus. Your drawing might look like the following.

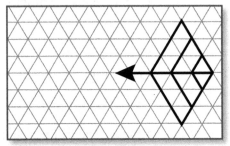

1. What do you notice about the diagonal?

2. Choose another set of three similar quadrilaterals from those you found in the Start It Off. Predict whether the same thing will be true of the diagonal from the nested vertex to the opposite vertex. Again, trace around your three similar shapes on the square or triangular grid paper, matching one of the corresponding angles. Draw the diagonal from the nested vertex. Do the diagonals of all three shapes lie on the same line? Compare your findings with a partner.

3. Nest the three triangles in a similar fashion. What do you notice?

4. Cut out the shapes on Lesson Guide 2.5 *Are These Shapes Similar?* Use what you know about similar shapes to determine which shapes are similar. Discuss with a partner different ways that you might determine this.

Which shapes are similar?

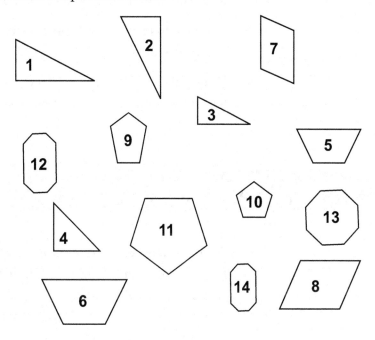

Dilations on a Coordinate Grid

MATHEMATICALLY SPEAKING

▶ scale factor

 **Let's Review** The scale factor is a number used as a multiplier to either enlarge or reduce the dimensions of an original object. It can be used to form dilations of geometric shapes.

As one of the architects at Accent on Architecture , you have a client who wants their storefront designed using pentagon shapes. You decide to use a coordinate grid to help lay out the design.

5. Plot the following points on a coordinate grid. Draw line segments to connect the points in order and draw a line segment to connect the last point to the first point.

    $A\ (0, 0), B\ (6, 0), C\ (9, 3), D\ (3, 6), E\ (-3, 3)$

6. Use a scale factor of $\frac{1}{3}$ to create a new pentagon. To do this, multiply each x- and y-coordinate by $\frac{1}{3}$. Label the vertices A', B', C', D' and E' and connect them in order, also connecting the last point to the first point. List each of the coordinates.

7. Create another pentagon using a scale factor of 2, based on the pentagon $A'B'C'D'E'$. List the coordinates and label them $A''B''C''D''E''$.

8. You have decided to use the pentagon $A''B''C''D''E''$ as a door placed in the center of the base of the original pentagon. Describe a transformation to help you lay this out on the grid.

9. You plan to use the small pentagon as a window in the design, centered at the very top of your design. Describe a transformation to do this.

10. Draw your final design using the pentagons and transformations you have described. Are all the pentagons similar? How do you know?

Designing Using Dilations and Transformations

11. As a new marketing promotion, Accent On Architecture  is going to feature a storefront design with repeated uses of the same shape. Choose a different shape (other than a pentagon) and design a storefront based on this shape. Describe transformations of this shape that could be used to represent doors and windows.

12. Trade descriptions with a partner and sketch each other's buildings on a coordinate grid. Check with your partner to see if your sketch matches the intended design.

⇧W rap It Up

Describe three ways to determine if two polygons are similar. Include examples and sketches.

On Your Own

 **Write About It**

1. Rectangle A has sides of 3 cm and 8 cm. Rectangle B has dimensions of 2 cm and 6 cm.

   a) Describe how you might determine if the two rectangles are similar using nesting.

   b) Describe how you might determine if the two rectangles are similar using proportions.

   c) Describe how you might determine if the two rectangles are similar using a coordinate grid.

2. Cut out rectangles with the following dimensions:

   • 3 cm by 4.5 cm

   • 6 cm by 10 cm

   • 9 cm by 15 cm

   • 4 cm by 6 cm

   • 4.5 cm by 7.5 cm

   a) Which rectangles are similar to the 6 cm by 10 cm rectangle? Explain how you know.

   b) Are the remaining rectangles similar to each other? Explain.

3. Holly made this polygon using the pattern blocks and said it is similar to the original rhombus.

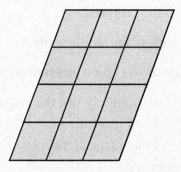

   Is she right? Explain.

4. Plot triangle *ABC* with coordinates *A* (2, 3), *B* (0, 0) and *C* (−2, 3).

a) Using a scale factor of 3, plot triangle *A'B'C'* that is the image of the original triangle.

b) Using a scale factor of $\frac{1}{2}$, plot triangle *A"B"C"* that is another image of the original triangle.

c) Are your three triangles similar? How do you know?

d) What if you use a scale factor of 3 on sides *AB* and *BC* and a scale factor of 2 on side *AC*? Predict what the new triangle will look like. Will it be similar to the original?

5. Plot rectangle *DEFG* on a coordinate grid, with a length of 4 units and a width of 2 units.

a) List the coordinates of your rectangle.

b) Plot another rectangle, *D'E'F'G'*, with a length of 6 units and a width of 3 units. List the coordinates.

c) Describe a series of transformations that show the similarity of the two rectangles.

6. Suppose you use a scale factor to make an image of a given polygon.

a) If you use a scale factor of 1, how will the image of a polygon compare to the original? Will it be similar?

b) What do you know about the scale factor if the image is an enlargement of the original?

c) What do you know about the scale factor if the image is a reduction of the original?

d) How many similar polygons are possible? Explain.

7. Suppose you plot a given polygon on a coordinate grid.

a) If you multiply just the *x*-coordinate of each vertex by a scale factor of 2 and leave the *y*-coordinates of the vertices the same, how will the image compare to the original? Will the two polygons be similar?

b) If you multiply just the *y*-coordinate of each vertex of the original polygon by a scale factor less than 1 and leave the *x*-coordinates the same, how will this image compare to the original? Will these two polygons be similar?

8. Emma plotted a given polygon on a coordinate grid. She then divided each *x*- and *y*-coordinate of each vertex by $\frac{1}{3}$, and plotted this image. Was the image a reduction or enlargement of the original? Explain.

9. The Accent on Architecture  firm designed the building below and has lost the original plans with the measurements. They know that the man in the picture is six feet tall. What are the length, width and height of the building? Explain your reasoning.

Think Beyond

10. Help the Accent on Architecture firm design a playground using at least three sets of similar polygons. Use a scale factor of $\frac{1}{48}$. That means that $\frac{1}{4}$ inch on your drawing will represent 1 foot on the actual playground. Include a key for your design and explain how you know that your shapes are similar.

Think Back

11. A store has marked the sale price of a sweater as 50% off. Today only, the store is taking an additional 50% off the marked sale price. Jayden takes the sweater to the clerk and asks to get it free. He says that 50% plus 50% is 100%, so the reduction is 100%. The clerk tells him that he has to pay $10 for the sweater.

    a) Was Jayden right? Explain.

    b) If the clerk is right, what was the original cost of the sweater?

12. On November 1, 2007, Peter Rosendahl of Sweden set a world record riding a unicycle for a distance of 5.79 m. The diameter of the unicycle wheel was only 15 mm! If the unicycle had no gears, how many times did Peter have to turn the wheel? Show your work.

13. Jerilyn walked the first 3 miles of her hike in 45 minutes and the last 2 miles in an hour. What was her average speed in miles per hour for the 5 miles she walked?

14. Paulina is 2 years older than May and 5 years younger than Peter. If you add all their ages together, the total is 39. How old is May? Show your work.

15. The Math Club spent $112 buying 10 math games. The Geo-Genius games were $12 each and the Algebra Antics games were $10 each. How many of each game did they buy? Show your work.

Optional Technology Lesson for this section available in your eBook

Sum It Up

In this section, you explored congruence and similarity of polygons. Specifically, you learned about relationships among angles and sides in triangles and special properties that help determine the congruence and similarity of triangles. You explored the effects and properties of transformations, including reflections, translations, rotations and dilations, on any two-dimensional figure with and without the use of a coordinate grid.

Congruent Triangles

■ Two triangles are congruent if the sides and angles of one triangle are equal in measure to the corresponding sides and angles of the other triangle. For the congruent triangles below, we say $\triangle ABC \cong \triangle DEF$.

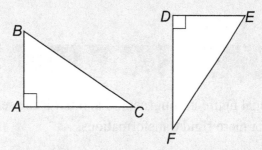

We can then write congruence statements for corresponding parts of the two triangles.

$m\angle A = m\angle D$ or $\angle A \cong \angle D$ $\overline{AB} \cong \overline{DE}$ or $AB = DE$

$m\angle B = m\angle E$ or $\angle B \cong \angle E$ $\overline{BC} \cong \overline{EF}$ or $BC = EF$

$m\angle C = m\angle F$ or $\angle C \cong \angle F$ $\overline{AC} \cong \overline{DF}$ or $AC = DF$

■ **Side-Side-Side Property or SSS Property.** If three sides of one triangle are congruent to three sides of another triangle, then the triangles are congruent.

Using this property, you can conclude that two triangles below are congruent.

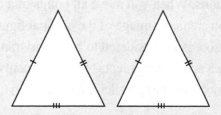

- **Side-Angle-Side Property or SAS Property.** If two sides and an included angle of one triangle are congruent to two sides and an included angle of another, then the triangles are congruent.

  Using this property, you can conclude that two triangles below are congruent.

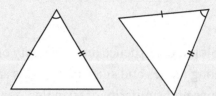

- **Angle-Side-Angle Property or ASA Property.** If two angles and the included side of one triangle are congruent to two angles and the included side of another, then the triangles are congruent.

  Using this property, you can conclude that two triangles below are congruent.

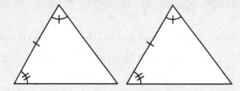

Congruence

- A two-dimensional figure is congruent to another if the second one can be obtained from the first by one or more rigid transformations.

- Polygons are congruent if they have the same shape, with all corresponding angles and all corresponding sides congruent.

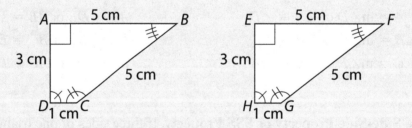

Quadrilaterals *ABCD* and *EFGH* are congruent.

- **Rigid Transformations.** When you move all points of a figure in a plane according to a common rule or operation, you create an image of the original figure. If the image is congruent to the original figure, the process is considered to be a rigid transformation. In rigid transformations, lines are taken to lines and line segments to line segments of the same length; angles are taken to angles of the same measure; and parallel lines are taken to parallel lines.

There are three types of rigid transformations.

■ **Translation.** A translation slides each point of a figure the same distance and same direction.

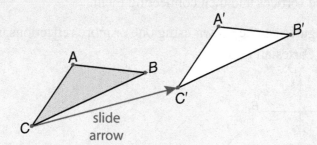

Triangle $A'B'C'$ is the image of triangle ABC after a translation. The slide arrow shows the distance and direction of the move.

■ **Rotation.** A rotation turns each point of a figure in the same direction, by the same angle, around the same center of rotation.

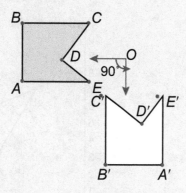

Pentagon $A'B'C'D'E'$ is the image of pentagon $ABCDE$ after a rotation of 90° counterclockwise around point O.

■ **Reflection.** A reflection flips each point of a figure over a line, called the reflection line, or line of symmetry.

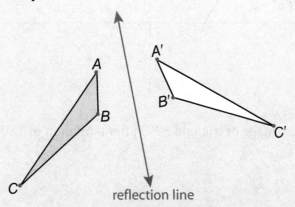

Triangle $A'B'C'$ is the image of triangle ABC after a reflection over the reflection line.

■ A polygon can be plotted on a Cartesian coordinate grid by plotting the ordered pairs that represent the vertices and then connecting them.

■ Congruence of figures can be shown using one or more reflections, rotations, and/or translations on a Cartesian grid.

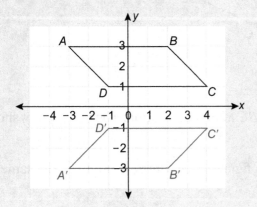

Parallelogram $A'B'C'D'$ is a reflection over the x-axis of parallelogram $ABCD$.

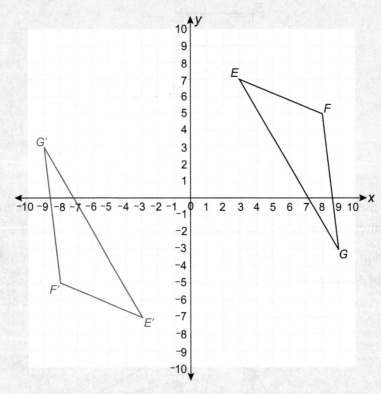

Triangle $E'F'G'$ is the image of triangle EFG after a rotation of 180° clockwise about the origin.

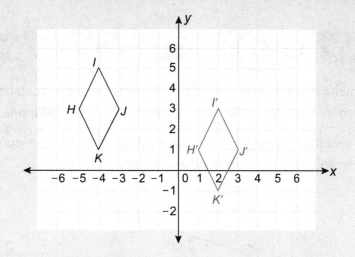

Parallelogram $H'I'J'K'$ is a translation 6 spaces to the right and 2 spaces down of parallelogram $HIJK$.

Similarity of figures can be shown using one or more dilations, rotations, reflections and/or translations on a Cartesian grid.

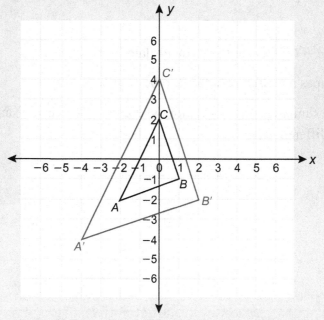

Triangle $A'B'C'$ is a dilation of triangle ABC with a scale factor of 2.

Similarity

- A two-dimensional figure is similar to another if the second can be obtained from the first by one or more rotations, reflections, translations, and/or dilations.

- Polygons are similar if they have the same shape, with all corresponding angles congruent and all corresponding sides proportional in length.

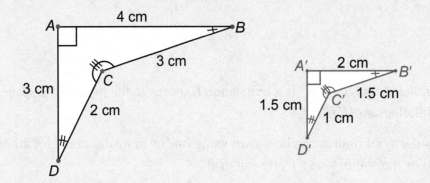

Quadrilateral $A'B'C'D'$ is similar to quadrilateral $ABCD$.

- Congruent shapes are also considered to be similar.

- A dilation is a similarity transformation where the image is the same shape as the original but may be a different size.

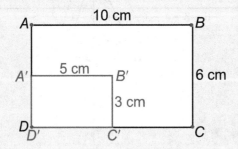

Rectangle $A'B'C'D'$ is a dilation of rectangle $ABCD$ using a scale factor of $\frac{1}{2}$.

- A scale factor is a number used as a multiplier to enlarge or reduce the dimensions of an original object. It can be used to form dilations of geometric figures.

Similar Triangles

Similar triangles have corresponding congruent angles and their corresponding sides are in proportion. The symbol ~ means "is similar to."

We name similar triangles using three letters in the order of their corresponding angles.

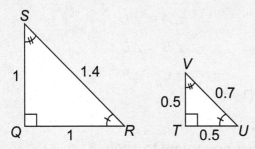

$$\triangle QRS \sim \triangle TUV$$

$$\angle Q \cong \angle T$$

$$\angle R \cong \angle U$$

$$\angle S \cong \angle V$$

$$\frac{SQ}{VT} = \frac{SR}{VU} = \frac{RQ}{UT}$$

 NOTE All congruent triangles are similar since their angles are congruent and their corresponding sides are in proportion with a ratio of 1:1.

Angle-Angle-Angle (AAA) Similarity Property. If three angles of one triangle are equal in measure to three angles of another triangle, then the triangles are similar.

Angle-Angle (AA) Similarity Theorem. If two angles of one triangle are equal in measure to two angles of another triangle, then the triangles are similar.

Since the angle measures of all triangles sum to 180°, the third angles of each of these pairs of triangles will also be congruent.

MATHEMATICALLY SPEAKING

Do you know what these mathematical terms mean?

- acute triangle
- Angle-Angle (AA) Similarity Theorem
- Angle-Angle-Angle Similarity (AAA) Property
- Angle-Side-Angle (ASA) Property
- congruent figures
- congruent triangles
- corresponding angles
- corresponding sides
- dilation
- equiangular triangle
- equilateral triangle
- flip

- image
- included angle
- included side
- isosceles triangle
- obtuse triangle
- pentomino
- proportion
- ratio
- reflection
- right triangle
- reflection line (line of symmetry)
- rotation
- rigid transformation

- scale factor
- scalene triangle
- Side-Angle-Side (SAS) Property
- Side-Side-Side (SSS) Property
- similar figures
- similar triangles
- slide
- symbol "⊥"
- symbol "~"
- transformation
- translation
- trigonometry
- turn

Part 1. What did you learn?

1. Name the corresponding sides in the pair of triangles below.

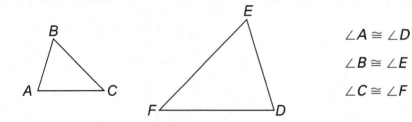

$\angle A \cong \angle D$

$\angle B \cong \angle E$

$\angle C \cong \angle F$

2. In two triangles, *BAT* and *FLY*, angle *B* is congruent to angle *F* and angle *A* is congruent to angle *L*.

   a. Is this enough information to conclude that the triangles are congruent? Why or why not?

   b. Is this enough information to conclude that the triangles are similar? Why or why not?

3. Isaiah has been absent for a few days. When he returns, his teacher tells him about the AA Similarity Theorem. Isaiah asks, "Is this theorem a rule we just have to memorize? Or is there a reason why the theorem is true?" How would you respond to Isaiah so that he knows why the AA Similarity Theorem makes sense?

4. Is there enough information in the diagram below to find the length of side *z*? Why or why not? If you conclude that there is enough information, find the measure of side *z*.

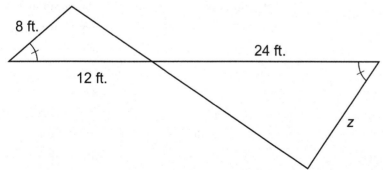

8 ft.

12 ft.

24 ft.

z

5. Dan wants to know if the triangles below are similar. Dan knows that the ratios of corresponding sides of similar triangles are equal. He wrote the proportion $\frac{24}{16} = \frac{18}{12}$, but he doesn't know how to determine whether these ratios are equivalent. What are some suggestions you would give to Dan?

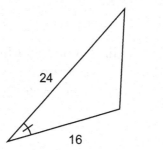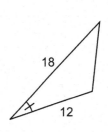

6. In the picture below, triangle *PQR* is similar to triangle *STU*.

    a. What is the length of side *ST*? Show or explain how you got your answer.

    b. What is the length of side *PR*? Show or explain how you got your answer.

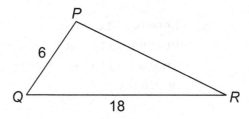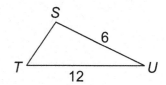

7. Can an obtuse triangle and a right triangle ever be congruent? If so, give an example. If not, explain why not.

8. Can an obtuse triangle and a right triangle ever be similar? If so, give an example. If not, explain why not.

9. Can an acute triangle and an isosceles triangle ever be congruent? Why or why not? If so, give an example. If not, explain why not.

10. Can an acute triangle and an isosceles triangle ever be similar? Why or why not? If so, give an example. If not, explain why not.

11. Match each picture to the correct description.

a. 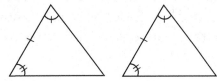

    i. These two triangles are congruent based on the Side-Side-Side Property.

b.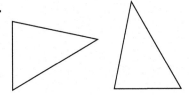

    ii. These two triangles are congruent based on the Side-Angle-Side Property.

c.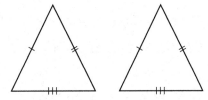

    iii. These two triangles are congruent based on the Angle-Side-Angle Property.

d.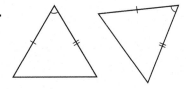

    iv. There is not enough information to determine if these two triangles are congruent.

12. Does the diagram below contain enough information to prove that triangles *ABC* and *DEF* are congruent? Why or why not?

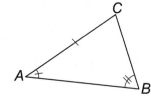 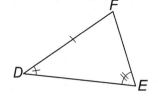

13. a. Khalil drew triangle *ABC*, and then translated it 5 units right and 1 unit down to form triangle *A′B′C′*. Given *A* (1, 1), *B* (3, 5), and *C* (4, 2), what are the coordinates of *A′*, *B′* and *C′*?

b. What do you know about the size, shape and location of Khalil's two triangles? Plot the two triangles on a Cartesian coordinate grid.

c. Rotate triangle *ABC* 90° counterclockwise around the origin to form triangle *A″B″C″*. List the coordinates of *A″*, *B″* and *C″*.

d. Using a scale factor of 2 on triangle *ABC*, form triangle *A‴B‴C‴* so that *A* and *A‴* are nested vertices. List the coordinates of the vertices. How does the perimeter of this triangle compare to the original? How does its area compare?

e. Reflect triangle *A‴B‴C‴* over the *x*-axis and label it *A″″B″″C″″*. Is triangle *A″″B″″C″″* similar to triangle *ABC*? How do you know?

14. Copy trapezoid *DEFG* onto triangular grid paper.

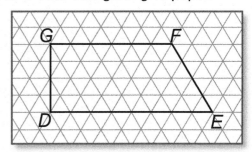

a. Using a scale factor of $\frac{1}{2}$, create a trapezoid similar to trapezoid *DEFG* and nest it inside this one on angle *D*.

b. Explain two different methods to show that these trapezoids are similar.

Part 2. What went wrong?

15. Dina was asked to explain the term *congruent* on a recent quiz. Dina wrote, "Two shapes are congruent if they are exactly the same size and shape." Her answer only received partial credit. What is wrong with Dina's answer? How could you help her improve her answer?

16. Hank plotted a pentagon in the first quadrant of a Cartesian grid and then reflected it over the *y*-axis to create its image. He said that the image was congruent to the original but was not similar, because similar shapes had to be different sizes. What would you tell Hank to correct his reasoning?

Exploring the Volume of Solids with Curved Surfaces

From designing containers to designing high-rise buildings, it is important to measure the capacity of an object: the maximum volume or amount of space that is available within the object. Artisans, engineers, contractors and architects are very much aware of this, and take volume into account as they create their designs. In this section, you will explore the volume of these three-dimensional shapes with curved surfaces: cylinders, cones and spheres. You will see how these shapes are used in the world around you. For example, architects design silos in the shape of cylinders, and we all know what ice cream cones look like.

LESSON 3.1 Cylinders

 Start It Off

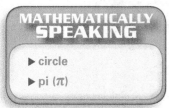
MATHEMATICALLY SPEAKING

▶ circle

▶ pi (π)

1. With your partner, discuss and write down the definition of a circle.

2. What is the relationship between the radius and the diameter of a circle?

3. Give two formulas for the circumference of a circle.

4. Find the circumference of a circle with a radius of 3.5 cm. Use 3.14 for π.

5. Explain the difference between the area of a circle and the circumference of a circle.

6. What is the formula for the area of a circle?

7. Find the area of a circle with a radius of 6.2 cm.

8. Find the area of a circle with a diameter of 13 in.

Finding the Volume of Cylinders

Accent on Architecture  has just been hired to design a new barn with a silo that will hold grain for Cornucopia Farms, Inc. In creating their designs for the silo, an important factor is the amount of grain that the silo will hold.

1. Talk to your partner to decide which mathematical concept (perimeter, area, surface area or volume) the architects should use to determine how much grain will fit in the silo.

2. A silo is in the shape of a circular cylinder. Name some other three-dimensional objects that have this shape. What are the mathematical characteristics of this shape?

Pasta, Anyone?

Let's start small. Have you ever been in a pizza place or Italian restaurant and seen a display of really large pasta jars? The jars are cylindrical, or in the shape of a cylinder. How much pasta do you think is in one jar? How might you estimate the number of pieces of pasta?

3. **Try it now!** Your teacher will pass around a filled jar of pasta. Working with a partner, estimate (without counting all the pieces) how many pasta pieces are in the jar. Be ready to share how you determined your answer.

You have actually been finding the volume of the cylindrical jar. Volume is the amount of space contained in an object. The formula for the volume of a circular cylinder is very similar to the formula for the volume of a prism, which you already know.

 **Let's Review**

To find the volume of a prism, you multiply the area of the base times the height. Remember, this is written as $V = Bh$, where B represents the area of the base. To find the area of the base of a rectangular prism, you multiply length times width. So sometimes we see the formula for the volume of a rectangular prism written as $V = l \cdot w \cdot h$.

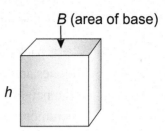

B (area of base)

h

To find the volume of a circular cylinder, you also multiply the area of the base by the height. The area of the base is the area of the circular bottom (or top), and the height relates to the number of layers of the base that make up the cylinder. Once again, B is the area of the circular base (or πr^2) and h represents the height of the cylinder.

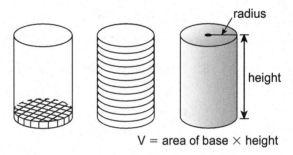

radius

height

$V = $ area of base $\times$ height

4. How are the formulas for the volume of a prism and a cylinder similar? How are they different?

 **Hint**
See page 155

Comparing Volumes

5. Get two identical pieces of notebook paper ($8\frac{1}{2}$ in. by 11 in.). Use tape to form two different paper cylinders with open bases.

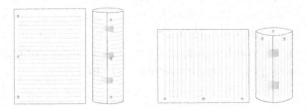

a) With your partner, predict which cylinder will hold more.

b) Use the volume formula to find out which cylinder holds more cubic inches. Compare this to your prediction.

c) **Try it!** Use sand or rice to fill one cylinder. Does the second cylinder hold the same amount, a greater amount or less than the first? How does this compare with the answers you found using the formulas?

6. Victor packs pickles into cylindrical jars. One jar has a diameter of 3 inches and a height of 5 inches. Another jar has a diameter of 5 inches and a height of 3 inches. Do the jars hold the same amount? If not, how much more does the larger jar hold than the smaller jar?

 Let's Review Remember, when you were studying the volume of prisms you learned that 1 cubic centimeter = 1 milliliter. Or 1 cm³ = 1 mL .

7. Victor's mother has cylindrical jars of sour pickles that hold 2.57 liters each. The height of each jar is 15 cm.

a) Approximately how wide is the mouth of the jar?

b) Why can we measure the volume of the jar in liters, but its height and radius in centimeters?

8. Now let's go back to our task at Accent on Architecture 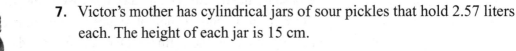. A typical silo is 60 ft tall with a diameter of 16 ft. If our design for the silo uses these dimensions, how much grain will the silo hold?

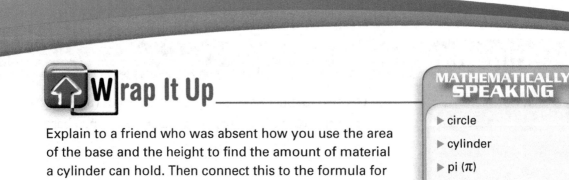

Wrap It Up_____

Explain to a friend who was absent how you use the area of the base and the height to find the amount of material a cylinder can hold. Then connect this to the formula for finding the volume of a cylinder. Use a cylindrical object or drawing of a circular cylinder to help you.

MATHEMATICALLY SPEAKING

▸ circle

▸ cylinder

▸ pi (π)

▸ volume

Use 3.14 or $\frac{22}{7}$ for π. Round answers to the nearest tenth.

Write About It

1. How is the volume for a circular cylinder similar to the general formula for finding the volume of a prism? Use pictures and words in your explanation.

2. Find an object in the shape of a cylinder in your home or at school. Draw a picture of the cylinder and label the dimensions. Determine the cylinder's volume.

3. The Cornucopia Farms silo designed by Accent on Architecture is 60 ft tall and has a diameter of 16 ft. Cornucopia Farms has a herd of 53 cattle. Each day, the herd eats enough grain to lower the height of the grain in the silo by two inches.

   a) What is the volume of grain that is removed daily?

   b) At this rate, how long will the grain in the silo last if the silo is filled to the top at the start of the first day?

4. Find the missing values.

   a) The pencil holder has a volume of approximately 1,469.5 cm³ and a diameter of 12 cm. What is its height?

   b) A coffee mug has a capacity of about 572 mL. The height of the mug is 9 cm. What is its radius?

   c) A bolt in the shape of a cylinder has a volume of about 14,949.5 cm³. The height of the bolt is 9 cm. Determine the radius and diameter of the bolt.

5. Snare drums come in different sizes, but most have a diameter of 14 inches. The three drums below vary in height.

   a) Determine the volume of each drum, assuming they are cylindrical. Round to the nearest tenth of a cubic inch.

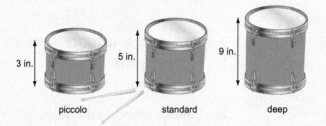

   3 in.   piccolo   5 in.   standard   9 in.   deep

   b) What fraction of the volume of the deep drum are the volumes of the piccolo and standard drums?

6. Elizabeth wants to make three candles to give to her grandparents as a gift. The cylindrical candles will be 4, 8 and 12 inches tall. They will all have a diameter of 3 inches. How much wax does she need to purchase?

7. Accent on Architecture uses mailing tubes to send their blueprint designs to clients. Find the price of the following mailing tubes.

Type of Tube	Inside Diameter	Length	Price ($0.01 per in.³)
Small	$1\frac{1}{2}$"	18"	
Medium	2"	12"	
Medium	2"	24"	
Large	$2\frac{1}{2}$"	12"	
Jumbo	4"	9"	

8. Vitabin, a new athletic drink, is packaged in cylindrical plastic bottles. An ad for Vitabin claims that a 6-pack of Vitabin contains 3 liters of liquid. The diameter of each bottle is 7 cm and the height is 13 cm. Is the Vitabin ad accurate? Do you get 3 liters of liquid in every 6-pack?

9. The Alaska Pipeline is a major oil pipeline connecting all of the oil fields in northern Alaska to a seaport in Valdez. From there the oil can be shipped to the rest of the United States. The Pipeline is 4 feet in diameter and 799 miles long. How much oil can be inside the Pipeline at one time?

   Hint
   See page 155

Think Beyond

10. Which shape has the greater volume—a cylinder with a base diameter greater than its height, or a cylinder with a height greater than the diameter of the base?

Think Beyond

11. One cylinder has radius r and height h. Another cylinder has radius h and height r. Do the cylinders have the same volume? Explain your answer.

Think Back

12. **a)** Will you save more money buying a $40.00 pair of jeans at 20% off or a $30.00 long-sleeved top at 15% off? Show your work.

b) In Question 12a, which purchase will have the lowest final price?

13. What three-dimensional shapes have congruent, parallel bases? Name four examples.

14. Round each number and give an approximate answer. Then, find the exact answer.

a) $0.2745 + (-1.4777)$

b) $36 - 17.9302$

c) $\frac{5}{6} \cdot -15.1 \cdot -2^2 \cdot \frac{-12}{10}$

15. The diameter of a circle has the same length as two radii. Ozzie used the following formula to find the area of a circle with a diameter of 7 cm: $A = \pi \frac{1}{2} d^2$. He used 3.14 for the value of π. Check Ozzie's work. Find, describe and fix any errors.

$A = \pi(\frac{1}{2} \cdot 7)^2$

$A = \pi(\frac{1}{2} \cdot 49)$

$A = \pi (24.5)$

$A = 76.93 \text{ cm}^2$

16. Franklin says that when you subtract two negative integers, the order of the integers doesn't affect the difference. Do you agree or disagree with Franklin? Why?

Cones

➡ Start It Off

Two students were discussing the value of π.

π is equal to 3.14.

I disagree. I think that π is equal to $\frac{22}{7}$.

1. List everything you know about π. What does π represent?

2. Is π a rational number? Is it a real number? How do we classify π?

3. What is the value of π? Why are the area and circumference of circles approximate measures?

4. How can we write exact values for the area and circumference of circles? Give an example.

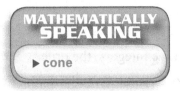

MATHEMATICALLY SPEAKING

▶ **cone**

A **cone** is a three-dimensional figure that has a single curved base and one vertex, called an apex. The cones in this book have circular bases. The height of a cone is perpendicular from the center of the base to the apex of the cone.

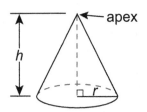

apex

h

r

Some objects are in the shape of cones. The "cone" of an ice cream cone is an example. Traffic cones are used to direct traffic, indicate cross walks and show boundaries on playing fields. Many funnels are in the shape of cones.

Finding the Volume of Cones

1. Examine the cylinder and cone below that have congruent bases and the same height. Guess what fraction of the volume of the cylinder is equal to the volume of the cone.

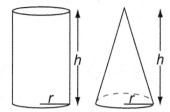

2. Use your geometric volume blocks of the cone and the cylinder. Fill the cone with rice or water and pour what's in the cone into the cylinder. About what fraction of the cylinder is filled? Do this again until the cylinder is full. How many times do you have to fill the cone?

3. Examine another cone and cylinder with congruent bases and the same height. About what fraction of the volume of the cylinder is the cone's volume?

4. Give the formula for the volume of a cone using what you know about the volume of a cylinder.

rap It Up

MATHEMATICALLY
SPEAKING

▶ cone

Explain how to use the formula for the volume of a cone to solve the following problem.

- The "jumbo" ice cream cone at Sam's Ice Cream Shop has a diameter of 12 cm and a height of 12 cm. When ice cream scoops are piled onto the cone, it holds 4 times the volume of the cone alone. How much ice cream is in a jumbo cone?

 Use 3.14 or $\frac{22}{7}$ for π. Round answers to the nearest tenth.

Write About It

1. Katie and Jonas each found the volume of the cone below but got different answers. They decided their answers were different because Katie used 15 cm as the height and Jonas used 12 cm as the height.

   a) Explain to Katie and Jonas who is correct and why.

   b) Find the volume of the cone.

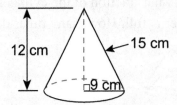

12 cm   15 cm

9 cm

2. Determine the volume of the following cones.

   a)

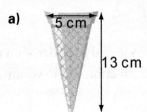

   5 cm

   13 cm

   b)

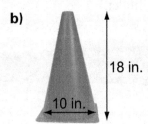

   18 in.

   10 in.

3. a) Popcorn is sold in three different cylinder-like containers, but the containers are not perfect cylinders. Find their approximate volumes.

i)

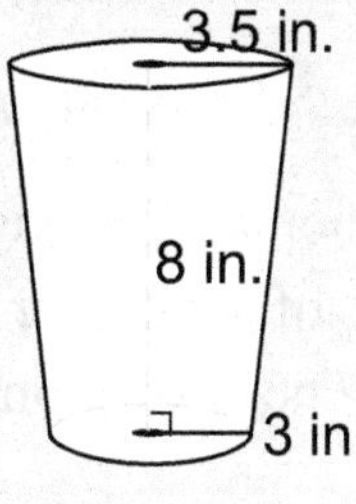

3.5 in.

8 in.

3 in.

$2.80 each

ii)

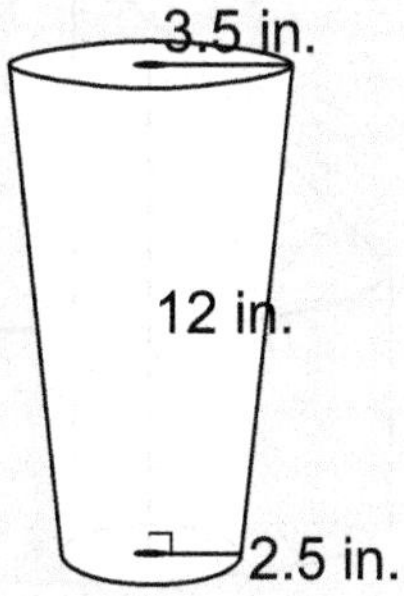

3.5 in.

12 in.

2.5 in.

$2.60 each

iii)

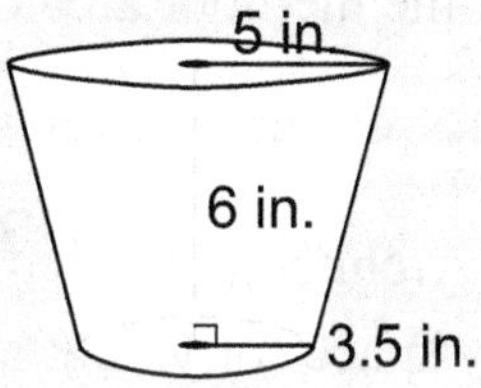

5 in.

6 in.

3.5 in.

$2.50 each

b) Explain your strategy for determining the volume of the container in Part ii.

c) Which container is the best buy?

4. The cups at the school's water cooler are paper cones. They are 2.5 inches in diameter and 3 inches deep. How much water does one of these cups hold?

5. The volume of each cone is given. Find the missing values.

   a) $V \approx 127$ cm^3, $h = 8$ cm, $r =$ _____

   b) $V \approx 804$ ft.^{3}, $d = 16$ ft., $h =$ _____

6. For centuries, nomadic Mongolians have lived in dwellings called yurts. A yurt consists of a cylinder and a cone. They are easily taken apart and moved to a new location. Today people build yurts using modern materials.

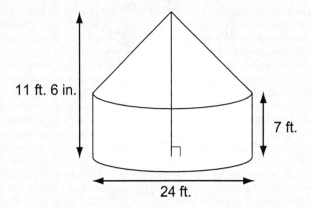

   a) Determine the floor area of the yurt.

   b) Find the volume of air inside the yurt. Explain your solution.

7. Accent on Architecture 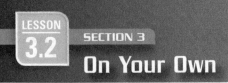 has been commissioned to create an indoor play space for young children at Sunshine Day Care Center. They have decided to make it in the shape of a yurt. It should not take up an entire room. Decide on dimensions for the yurt, draw a model and then determine the floor area and volume.

Think Beyond

8. Find how to calculate the surface area of a cylinder and a cone.

9. If two sides of a right triangle have lengths of 3 cm and 4 cm, what is the length of the third side? Is there more than one possible length for the third side? If so, list all possible lengths.

10. Give the slope and the y-intercept of the line represented by each equation.

   a) $y = 3x - 2$ **b)** $y = x - 2$ **c)** $y = -x$

11. Write each equation in $y = mx + b$ form.

   a) $2y = -4x + 8$

   b) $-y + 4 = x$

   c) $3x - 2 = 4 + y$

12. $5 - (2 - 6) =$

   A. 1   **C.** 9

   B. -9   **D.** 13

13. In a classroom of 24 students, 8 wear glasses or contacts. If one student is chosen at random, what is the probability that the student does not wear glasses or contacts?

Spheres

➡ Start It Off

Solve for *x*.

1. $\frac{2}{3}x = 8$

2. $\frac{3}{4}x + 9 = 27$

3. $72 = 1\frac{1}{2}x$

4. $\frac{3}{5}x - 4 = \frac{1}{5}$

5. $7 = \frac{1}{3}x + \frac{2}{3}$

6. $\frac{1}{2}x = a$

7. $\frac{2}{3}x = r$

8. Talk to your partner. Explain how to solve an equation for a given variable when it is multiplied by a fraction.

This is a photo of the exterior of the Naismith Basketball Hall of Fame in Springfield, Massachusetts. In order to create this, the architects needed to know the properties of spheres, including their volume.

A Closer Look at Spheres

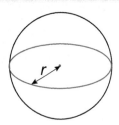

MATHEMATICALLY SPEAKING

▶ sphere

1. What are the attributes of spheres? Talk to your partner and list them. Then create a formal, mathematical definition of a sphere.

 **Hint**
See page 155

The Volume of Spheres and Cylinders

2. Think about a can of tennis balls. Do you think the volume of a sphere is the same as, less than or greater than the volume of a cylinder with the same height and radius?

a) Talk with your partner and come to a conclusion.

b) If you think the volumes are not the same, predict what fractional component one volume is of the other. For example, is the sphere half the volume of the cylinder? Is the cylinder one-third the volume of the sphere?

3. Let's find out the exact relationship between the volume of a sphere and the volume of a cylinder. Use your geometric volume blocks of a sphere and a cylinder that have the same radius, with the height of the cylinder twice the radius.

- Fill a half-sphere or hemisphere with water, rice or sand. Then pour the contents into the cylinder.

- Predict how many more fills of the hemisphere are needed to fill the cylinder.

- Test your prediction.

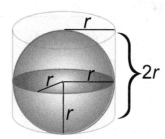

You should have discovered that 3 hemispheres of material fill the cylinder with the same radius and height as the sphere.

4. Complete the following statements.

a) The Volume of 3 Hemispheres = the Volume of _____ Spheres with the same radius.

b) _____ times the Volume of a Sphere = the Volume of a Cylinder.

c) So the Volume of a Sphere = _____ times the Volume of a Cylinder.

5. Write a formula for the volume of a sphere in terms of the radius. Use the formula for the volume of a cylinder to help you.

 **Hint**
See page 155

6. Perform the same experiment with the geometric volume blocks of a cone and a sphere. Notice that these blocks have the same radius, and the height of the cone is twice the length of the radius.

   Which do you think holds more, the cone or the sphere? Make a prediction with your partner.

7. Test your prediction by filling the hemisphere and pouring the contents into the cone.

8. What did you discover about the relationship between the volume of the cone and the sphere? Use this relationship to write a formula for the volume of the sphere in terms of the radius. Compare this with the formula you derived for the volume of a sphere using the cylinder.

Wrap It Up

Their teacher said they were all correct. How can this be? Talk to your partner.

MATHEMATICALLY SPEAKING

▶ hemisphere

▶ sphere

I learned that the volume of a sphere is $\frac{4}{3}\pi r^3$.

The volume of a sphere is $\frac{2}{3}$ the volume of a cylinder with the same radius and a height that is twice the radius of the sphere. So the volume of a sphere is $\frac{2}{3} \times \pi r^2 h$.

I found the volume of a sphere is twice the volume of a cone with the same radius and a height twice the radius of the sphere. So the volume of a sphere is $2 \times \frac{1}{3}\pi r^2 h$.

On Your Own

 Use 3.14 or $\frac{22}{7}$ for π. Round answers to the nearest tenth.

 **Write About It**

1. Explain how to find the volume of a sphere using either the formula for the volume of a cylinder or the formula for the volume of a cone. Assume that the cone and the cylinder have the same radius as the sphere, and the height of each is twice the radius. Include diagrams and formulas in your explanation.

2. Mina is making a jack-o-lantern. She is going to carve out and collect all of the pulp inside the pumpkin first, to save and cook later.

   She has a cube container with edges measuring 6 in. Her pumpkin is really close to the shape of a sphere and has a diameter of 6 inches. Assuming that the pulp inside the pumpkin is about two-thirds the total volume of the pumpkin, can she fit all of the pulp inside her container? Show your work and explain your answer.

3. Find the approximate volume of the different types of melon below. Some are more spherical than others!

   a)

   The radius of this cantaloupe is 2.5 in.

   b)

   The radius of this watermelon is 7 cm.

   c)

   The radius of this watermelon is 4.2 in. and the length is 14.4 in.

    **Hint**
   See page 155

4. Find the volume of each of the following:

    a)

    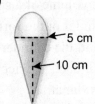

    ← 5.5 cm

    b)

    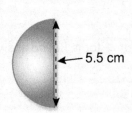

    ← 5 cm

    ← 10 cm

    c)

    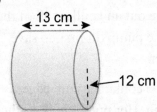

    ← 13 cm →

    ← 12 cm

5. 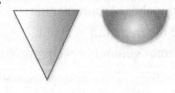 The cone and bowl both have the same diameter and the height of the cone is the same as the diameter of the bowl. Eliana thinks the cone will hold more pudding than the bowl. Steve disagrees and says the bowl will hold more. What do you think? Defend your reasoning.

6. If a sphere contains 904 cubic inches of space, what is its diameter?

7. A filled water balloon has the shape of a sphere with a diameter of 3.75 cm. How much water does this water balloon hold?

8. Two water tanks are shown. Tank A is a rectangular prism and Tank B is a cylinder. The tanks are not drawn to scale. Tank A is filled with water to the 8-meter mark. This water is then transferred to Tank B. If it fills Tank B to a height of 9 meters, what is the approximate radius of Tank B?

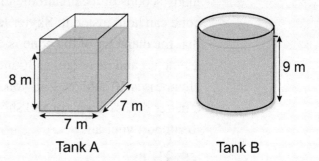

Tank A   Tank B

a) 14 m   c) 44 m

b) 12 m   d) 4 m

Think
Beyond

9. Accent on Architecture has been asked to create space-saving packaging for soccer balls. They need to pack individual balls very tightly in the container, so that the ball fills up as much of the space as possible. Would it be better to use a cube or a cylinder for the container? Explain your answer.

10. An igloo is in the shape of a hemisphere. The floor of this igloo has a diameter of 24 feet. Find the area of the floor and the total volume of the igloo.

11. There is a contest at the Udderly Frozen Ice Cream Shop to estimate how many scoops of ice cream the giant cone can hold inside it. Skyler learned that the diameter of the cone is 20 inches and its height is 30 inches. He guesses 50 scoops. Can you make a better guess? Explain and show work to support your answer.

 ? Hint
See page 155

 **Think Back**

12. The circle is inscribed in a square with 3-cm side lengths. What is the area of the shaded region? Use 3.14 for π.

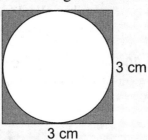

3 cm

3 cm

13. Find the missing numbers in this pattern. Is this an arithmetic or geometric sequence? Explain.

3, 6, _____, 24, _____, _____, 192

14. The perimeter of a rectangle is 28 units. If the width is 4 units, what is its area?

   A. 28 square units   **C.** 40 square units

   B. 14 square units   **D.** 49 square units

15. For the equation $y = {}^-2x - 7$, solve for x using the given y-values. Show your work.

   a) $y = {}^-19, x = ?$ **c)** $y = 5, x = ?$

   b) $y = {}^-1, x = ?$ **d)** $y = 13, x = ?$

16. Rebecca made the following table of her rope jumping:

Time	10 seconds	20 seconds	30 seconds	40 seconds	50 seconds
Number of Jumps	18 jumps	37 jumps	55 jumps	72 jumps	87 jumps

a) Plot these points on a graph. Label your axes.

b) How many times do you think she jumped in 25 seconds? In a minute? Give your reasoning.

c) Is it easier to get your answer from the table or the graph?

Optional Technology Lesson for this section available in your eBook

Sum It Up

Cylinders

■ Cylinders have two parallel bases that are congruent circles. The dimensions of a cylinder are the radius (or diameter) of the base and the height perpendicular to the base.

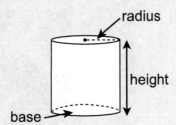

■ The formula for the volume of a cylinder can be found by multiplying the area of the base by the height of the cylinder. $V = \pi r^2 h$

> **Example 1**
>
> $V_{\text{cylinder}} = B \cdot h$ B represents the area of the base.
>
> $\phantom{V_{\text{cylinder}}} = \pi r^2 \cdot h$
>
> $\phantom{V_{\text{cylinder}}} = \pi (3^2)(5)$
>
> $\phantom{V_{\text{cylinder}}} = 45\pi$
>
> $\phantom{V_{\text{cylinder}}} \approx 141.3 \text{ cm}^3$
>
>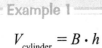
>
> The volume of the cylinder is 45π cubic centimeters or approximately 141.3 cm³.

Cones

- Cones have one base in the shape of a circle. The dimensions of a cone are the radius (or diameter) of the base and the height perpendicular to the base. The apex is the vertex of the cone.

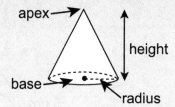

- The formula for the volume of a cone is one-third the volume of a cylinder with the same-size base and height. $V = \frac{1}{3}\pi r^2 h$

Example 2

$$V_{\text{cone}} = \frac{1}{3}Bh \qquad \text{\textit{B} represents the area of the base of the cone.}$$

$$= \frac{1}{3}(9\pi)5$$

$$= 15\pi$$

$$\approx 47.1 \text{ cm}^3$$

The volume of the cone is one-third the volume of the cylinder with a radius of 3 cm and a height of 5 cm, or about 47.1 cm³.

Spheres

- A sphere consists of all points in space that are equidistant from a fixed point called the center. The dimension of a sphere is the radius (or diameter).

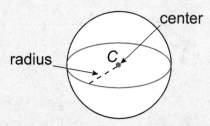

- The formula for the volume of a sphere is $V = \frac{4}{3}\pi r^3$.

- The volume of a sphere is $\frac{2}{3}$ the volume of a cylinder with the same radius as the sphere and a height twice the length of the radius.

$$V = \frac{2}{3}\pi r^2 (2r) = \frac{4}{3}\pi r^3$$

■ The volume of a sphere is twice the volume of a cone with the same radius and a height twice the length of the radius.

$$V = 2 \cdot \frac{1}{3}\pi r^2 (2r) = \frac{4}{3}\pi r^3$$

Example 3

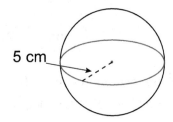

$$
\begin{aligned}
V_{\text{sphere}} &= \frac{4}{3}\pi r^3 \\
&= \frac{4}{3}(125)\,\pi \\
&= 166.67\pi \\
&\approx 523.33 \text{ cm}^3
\end{aligned}
$$

5 cm

The volume of the sphere is approximately 523.33 cm³.

MATHEMATICALLY SPEAKING

Do you know what these mathematical terms mean?

▶ circle   ▶ hemisphere   ▶ volume

▶ cone   ▶ pi (π)

▶ cylinder   ▶ sphere

Study Guide

**Exploring the Volume of Solids
with Curved Surfaces**

Part 1. What did you learn?

1. About how much fruit punch is in a full cylindrical can that is 15 cm tall and has a circumference of 26 cm? Use 3.14 for π.

2. If the volume of a cylinder is 18π cubic cm, what is the volume of a cone with the same base area and height? What is the volume of a sphere with the same radius as the cylinder? Show your work.

3. The radius of Earth is 3,960 miles. What is the volume of Earth?

4. A cylinder, cone and sphere all have the same radii. The heights of the cylinder and cone are the same, and both are equal to twice the height of the radius. Which solid can hold the most? Defend your reasoning. Write the volumes of the three solids in order from least to greatest.

5. Accent on Architecture is designing a building to house a carousel at the new Adventure Land park. They are going to use the design shown below. The height of the building to the apex of the cone roof is 20 feet. The height of the cylindrical part of the building is 12 feet and the radius is 20 feet. Find the volume of the building.

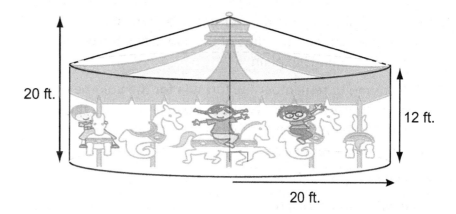

20 ft.

12 ft.

20 ft.

6. Which vase holds more water: a cylindrical vase with a diameter of 2.5 inches and a height of 4 inches, or a ball-shaped vase with a diameter of 3.5 inches? Show your work.

7. Fill in the blanks. Assume that all solids have the same radii and the heights of the cone and cylinder are both twice the height of the radius.

   A cone has one _____ while a cylinder has two _____ and a sphere has no _____.

   The volume of a _____ is half the volume of a sphere.

   The volume of a _____ is one-third the volume of a cylinder.

   The volume of a hemisphere is the same as the volume of a _____.

Part 2. What went wrong?

8. Daniella was asked the following question on a recent study quiz.

   > The circumference of the base of a cone is 14 cm.
   > The height of the cone is twice the radius. What is the volume of the cone?

   Daniella said she couldn't answer this question, since it did not include the length of the radius of the cone. What is wrong with Daniella's reasoning? Explain.

9. David is trying to remember the formula for the volume of a sphere. He thinks it is $\frac{2}{3}$ the volume of a cylinder with the same radius and a height that is double the length of the radius, so he writes the following:

   $$V = \frac{2}{3}(\pi r^2 h) = \frac{2}{3}(\pi r^2 \cdot 2r) = \frac{2}{3}(\pi \cdot 3r^3) = 2\pi r^3.$$

   Explain what went wrong.

Shape Up: Focusing on Triangles, Transformations and Measurement

Part 1. What did you learn?

1. Kalpita looked at a diagram that showed two parallel lines cut by a transversal. Each angle was identified with a number from 1 through 8. In the diagram, $m\angle 1 = 120°$. From this information, Kalpita figured out that $m\angle 2 = m\angle 3 = m\angle 4 = 120°$, and $m\angle 5 = m\angle 6 = m\angle 7 = m\angle 8 = 60°$.

   a. Sketch a diagram that matches this description. Label the angles with appropriate numbers.

   b. Explain why the angles that Kalpita describes are congruent.

2. An isosceles trapezoid has one pair of opposite congruent sides and one pair of opposite parallel sides. Answer each question about the isosceles trapezoid below.

   a. Which sides are congruent?

   b. Which sides are parallel?

   c. Which angles are supplementary? How do you know?

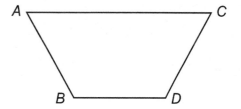

3. The diagram to the right can be used to prove the Triangle Sum Theorem: The sum of the interior angle measures of any triangle is 180°. In this diagram, line *l* is parallel to $\overline{UD}$.

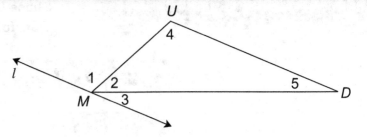

Write a formal proof of the Triangle Sum Theorem.

Statement	Justification

4. Match each description with the correct angle measure.

Description	Angle Measure
a. Measure of each interior angle in a regular hexagon	i) 360°
b. Interior angle sum of a 10-sided polygon	ii) 720°
c. Exterior angle sum of a square	iii) 1,440°
d. Measure of each interior angle in an equilateral triangle	iv) 120°
e. Interior angle sum of a hexagon	v) 60°

5. In scalene triangle *LET*, m∠L + m∠E = 80°. If m∠L = 48°, then m∠E = _____° and m∠T = _____°.

6. In isosceles triangle *DEF*, m∠D = m∠E and m∠F = 90°. So, m∠D = m∠E = _____°. We can conclude that triangle *DEF* is an isosceles _____ triangle.

7. In pentagon *ABCDE*, m∠A + m∠B + m∠C + m∠D = 508°. So, m∠E = _____°.

8. Without measuring, state whether or not each of the pairs of triangles is congruent. If the triangles are congruent, use the SSS Property, SAS Property or ASA Property to explain why.

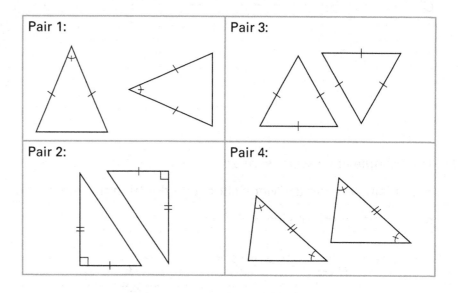

Pair 1:

Pair 3:

Pair 2:

Pair 4:

9. Imagine two triangles. One has vertices labeled *A*, *B* and *C* and the other has vertices labeled *D*, *E* and *F*. The following information is true: $\angle ABC \cong \angle DEF$, $\overline{AB} \cong \overline{DE}$ and $\angle BAC \cong \angle EDF$. Is this enough information to determine whether or not the triangles are congruent? Why or why not?

10. The triangles below are similar. Use a proportion to find *x*.

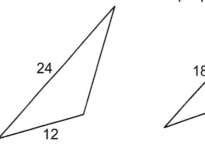

24

12

18

x

11. The triangles below are similar.

    a. Explain why the drawings show that the triangles are similar.

    b. Find the length of side *KL*.

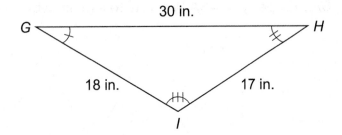

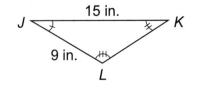

12. The triangles below are similar.

    a. Explain why the drawings show that the triangles are similar.

    b. Find the length of side *SU*.

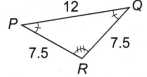

13. The coordinate plane below contains line segment *AB*. Copy this onto grid paper.

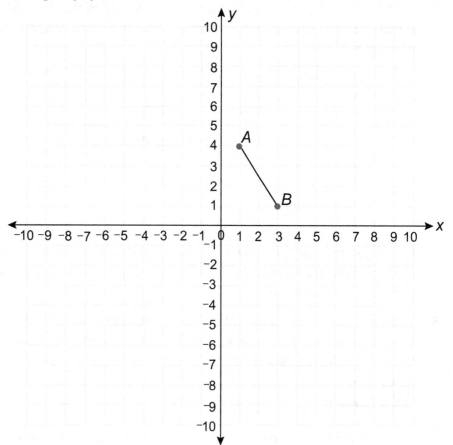

a. Use this line segment to create a non-rectangular parallelogram *ABCD*. List the coordinates of the vertices.

b. Find the area and perimeter of this parallelogram.

c. Reflect your parallelogram over the *x*-axis and label this *A′B′C′D′*. List the coordinates of the vertices. How do these coordinates compare to the coordinates of the original parallelogram?

d. Rotate parallelogram *A′B′C′D′* 90° counterclockwise about the origin and label the new parallelogram *A″B″C″D″*. List the coordinates of the vertices.

e. What are the areas and the perimeters of parallelograms *A′B′C′D′* and *A″B″C″D″*? Explain how you know these.

14. Find the volume of the cylinder formed by rolling the 13 × 17-inch piece of paper below. Use 3.14 for π and round your answer to the nearest tenth.

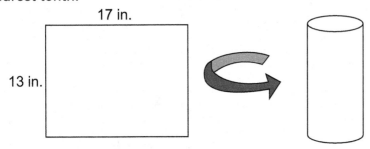

17 in.

13 in.

15. If a paper cone of the same height and diameter were inserted into the cylinder shown in Question 14, what would its volume be? How do you know?

16. Design a box in the shape of a yurt to package a set of children's blocks. Draw a diagram and label dimensions. Find the volume of the box to the nearest tenth.

 **Hint**
See page 155

17. Tennis balls have a diameter of 8 cm. Three tennis balls fit tightly against the interior, top and bottom of a cylindrical can. What is the volume of the can?

18. Explain how to find the formula for the volume of a sphere using either the formula for the volume of a cylinder or the formula for the volume of a cone.

19. Lucia measured all four angles of two different quadrilaterals and found that they were congruent to each other. She said that meant that the quadrilaterals must be similar to each other. What is wrong with Lucia's reasoning? Include a sketch of two quadrilaterals in your explanation.

20. Akinori was asked to answer the following question on his math test:

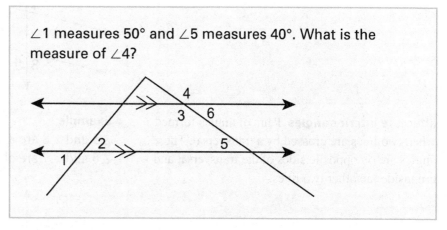

∠1 measures 50° and ∠5 measures 40°. What is the measure of ∠4?

Akinori wrote the following answer:

> If ∠1 is 50°, ∠2 must be 50°. This means that ∠4 must also be 50° because ∠1, ∠2, ∠3 and ∠4 are all vertical angles and vertical angles are always congruent.

What is wrong with Akinori's reasoning? What would you say or do to help him find and fix his error?

21. Alyse was asked to find the volume of a hemisphere with a circumference of 12 π cm. She did the following calculations.

$C = \pi d$. So $d = 12$.

Volume of the hemisphere is $\frac{1}{2}$ of a sphere.
So $V = \frac{1}{2} (\frac{4}{3} \pi \cdot 12^2)$

$V = \frac{2}{3} \pi \cdot 144$

$V = 96 \pi$ cu cm

Before she calculates her final answer, help Alyse find her errors.

acute triangle A triangle whose angle measures are each less than 90 degrees.

Example:

alternate exterior angles Pairs of angles formed when two lines are crossed by a transversal. These angles are on opposite sides of the transversal and are outside the other two lines.

Example:

∠1 and ∠4 are alternate exterior angles.
∠2 and ∠3 are also alternate exterior angles.

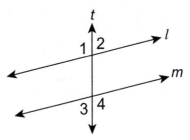

alternate interior angles Pairs of angles formed when two lines are crossed by a transversal. These angles are on opposite sides of the transversal and are inside the other two lines.

Example:

∠5 and ∠8 are alternate interior angles.
∠6 and ∠7 are also alternate interior angles.

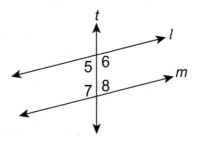

Angle-Angle (AA) Similarity Theorem The theorem that states that if two angles of one triangle are congruent to two angles of a second triangle, then the two triangles are similar.

Example:

△*ABC* ~ △*DEF* by the AA Theorem.

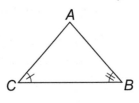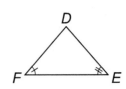

Angle-Angle-Angle (AAA) Similarity Property The property that states that if three angles of one triangle are congruent to three angles of a second triangle, then the two triangles are similar.

Example:

△*PQR* ~ △*STU* by the AAA Property.

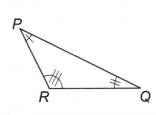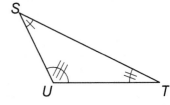

Angle-Angle-Side (AAS) Theorem The theorem that states that if two angles and a non-included side of one triangle are congruent to two angles and the corresponding non-included side of a second triangle, then the two triangles are congruent.

Example:

$\triangle JKL \cong \triangle MNO$ by the AAS Theorem.

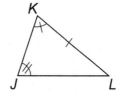
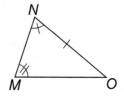

Angle-Side-Angle (ASA) Property The property that states that if two angles and the included side of one triangle are congruent to two angles and the included side of a second triangle, then the two triangles are congruent.

Example:

$\triangle ABC \cong \triangle DEF$ by the ASA Property.

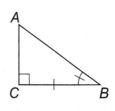
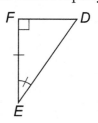

cone A three-dimensional shape that has a single curved base and an apex. A circular cone has a circle as a base.

Example:

cone

congruent Having the same size, shape and measure.

Example:

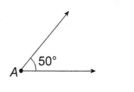

$\angle A$ **is congruent to** $\angle B$.

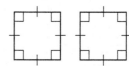

$\overline{AB}$ **is congruent to** $\overline{CD}$.

congruent figures Two figures are congruent if one can be obtained from the other by a series of rigid transformations (translations, reflections or rotations). These figures have the same shape and size; corresponding angles and corresponding lengths have the same measure.

Example:

corresponding angles Angles that have the same relative position in two related figures or objects.

Example:
Two related triangles: $\triangle ABC \cong \triangle DEF$. $\angle A$ corresponds to $\angle D$, $\angle B$ corresponds to $\angle E$ and $\angle C$ corresponds to $\angle F$.

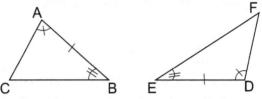

Two related intersections: Line t intersects parallel lines l and m. Corresponding angles are: $\angle 1$ and $\angle 5$, $\angle 2$ and $\angle 6$, $\angle 3$ and $\angle 7$, and $\angle 4$ and $\angle 8$.

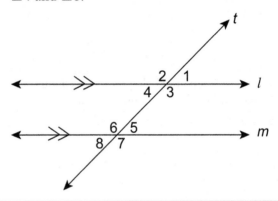

corresponding sides Sides that have the same relative position in two related figures.

Example:
$\triangle ABC \sim \triangle DEF$. $\overline{AB}$ corresponds to $\overline{DE}$, $\overline{BC}$ corresponds to $\overline{EF}$ and $\overline{CA}$ corresponds to $\overline{FD}$.

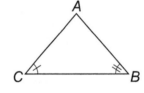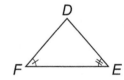

cylinder A three-dimensional shape with two parallel circular bases.

Example:

cylinder

dilation A similarity transformation that may enlarge or reduce a figure by a common scale factor but does not change the center point. The image is the same shape as the original but may be a different size. (Note that a simple translation with a scale factor of 1 is also considered a dilation.)

Example:
Triangle $A'B'C'$ is a dilation of triangle ABC with a center point at O.

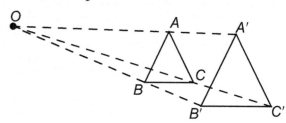

equiangular triangle A triangle whose angles are all of equal measure (60 degrees).

Example:
$\triangle ABC$ is equiangular.

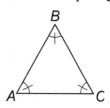

equilateral triangle A triangle whose sides are all of equal length.

Example:
$\triangle ABC$ is equilateral.

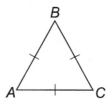

flip (reflection) A transformation that "flips" a figure over a "mirror" or reflection line.

Example:

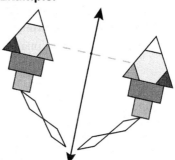

hemisphere A three-dimensional shape that is half a sphere and has a circular base.

Example:

image The result of a transformation.

Example:

Square $A'B'C'D'$ is the image of square $ABCD$.

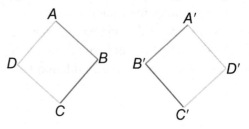

---

included angle An angle that is located between two adjacent sides in a figure.

Example:

In the figure below, $\angle B$ is included between sides $\overline{AB}$ and $\overline{BC}$.

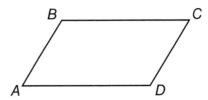

---

included side A side that is located between two adjacent angles in a figure.

Example:

In the figure below, side AB is included between $\angle A$ and $\angle B$.

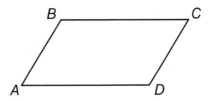

---

indirect measurement A method of measuring objects indirectly through the use of proportionality and similar triangles.

Example:

To find the height of the flagpole in the following diagram, we use indirect measurement with $\triangle ABC \sim \triangle DEF$ and lengths we can measure ($f = 6$ ft., $d = 9$ ft. and $a = 24$ ft.).

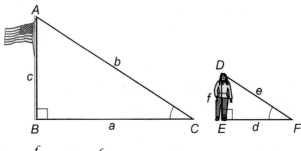

$$\frac{c}{a} = \frac{f}{d} \rightarrow \frac{c}{24} = \frac{6}{9} \rightarrow c = 16 \text{ ft.}$$

interior angles (of a polygon) The included angles (between two sides) on the interior of a polygon.

Example:
Angles 1, 2, 3 and 4 are the four interior angles of the trapezoid.

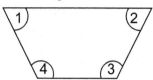

isosceles triangle A triangle with at least two sides equal in length.

Example:

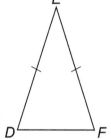

line of symmetry (reflection line) A line that acts as a mirror so that the corresponding points on either side are the same perpendicular distance from it.

Example:

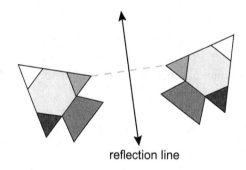

reflection line

obtuse triangle A triangle that has one angle with a measure greater than 90 degrees.

Example:

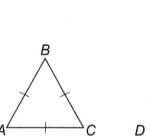

$m\angle B = 130°$ $m\angle D = 120°$

parallel Never intersecting. Everywhere the same perpendicular distance apart.

Example:

 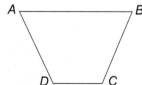

Lines m and n are parallel.   Sides $\overline{AB}$ and $\overline{CD}$ are parallel.

pentomino A two-dimensional figure consisting of five congruent squares connected along their sides.

Example:

A few of the possible pentominoes are shown below.

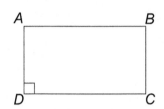

---

perpendicular Intersecting at a right angle.

Example:

Lines m and n are perpendicular.

Sides $\overline{AD}$ and $\overline{DC}$ are perpendicular.

---

pi (π) The ratio of the circumference of a circle and its diameter. Pi is indicated by the symbol π. Pi is an irrational number that is approximately equal to 3.14 or $\frac{22}{7}$.

---

proof A logical argument demonstrating that a mathematical statement is always true.

---

proportion An equation stating that two ratios are equal.

Example:

$\frac{a}{b} = \frac{c}{d}$ or $a : b = c : d$.

The corresponding sides of similar triangles are in proportion: $\frac{9}{12} = \frac{12}{16}$.

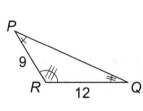

---

ratio A comparison or relationship between two quantities, a and b, stated as "a to b" and represented as $a{:}b$ or $\frac{a}{b}$ or as the single number quotient of $a \div b$.

Example:

The ratio representing the number of cars in a parking lot to the number of wheels is 1 to 4 and is represented by $\frac{1}{4}$ or 1 : 4 or 0.25.

---

reflection (flip) A transformation that "flips" a figure over a "mirror" or reflection line.

Example:
The figure on the left is a reflection of the figure on the right over the reflection line.

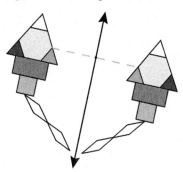

reflection line (line of symmetry) A line that acts as a mirror so that the corresponding points on either side are the same perpendicular distance from it.

Example:

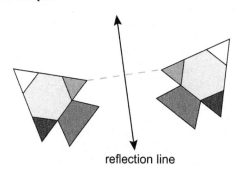

reflection line

reflexive property of equality The property that states that anything is equal to itself.

Example:
For all a, $a = a$.

$\overline{BD} = \overline{BD}$

$m\angle 1 = m\angle 1$

regular polygon A polygon that is equiangular (all angles of equal measure) and equilateral (all sides of equal measure).

Example:

right triangle A triangle that has one angle with a measure equal to 90 degrees.

Example:

rigid transformation A motion of points in space that preserves distance and angle measures. This consists of one or more reflections, rotations or translations.

Example:
Pentagon $A'B'C'D'E'$ is a rigid transformation of pentagon $ABCDE$.

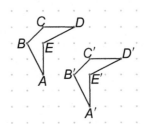

rotation (turn) A transformation that turns a figure about a given point in a specific direction and angle.

Example:
The figure at the top is a 90° counterclockwise rotation of the figure at the bottom around the vertex of the turn angle.

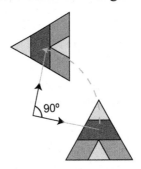

same-side interior angles Pairs of angles formed when two lines are crossed by a transversal. These angles are on the same side of the transversal and are inside the other two lines.

Example:
$\angle 5$ and $\angle 7$ are same-side interior angles.
$\angle 6$ and $\angle 8$ are also same-side interior angles.

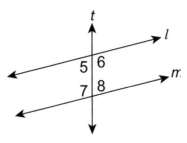

scale factor A number used as a multiplier to either enlarge or reduce the dimensions of an original object.

Example:

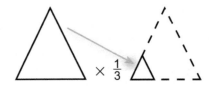

scalene triangle A triangle with no two sides of equal measure.

Example:

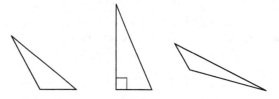

Side-Angle Inequality Property The property that states that if one side of a triangle is longer than another side, then the measure of the angle opposite the longer side is greater than the measure of the angle opposite the shorter side.

Example:

In the triangle below, $\overline{AB}$ is longer than $\overline{AC}$; therefore m$\angle C$ is greater than m$\angle B$.

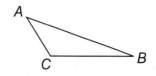

Side-Angle-Side (SAS) Property The property that states that if two sides and an included angle of one triangle are congruent to two sides and an included angle of a second triangle, then the two triangles are congruent.

Example:

$\triangle ABC \cong \triangle DEF$ by the SAS Property.

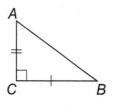
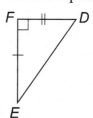

Side-Side-Side (SSS) Property The property that states that if three sides of one triangle are congruent to three sides of a second triangle, then the two triangles are congruent.

Example:

$\triangle PQR \cong \triangle STU$ by the SSS Property.

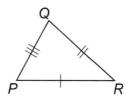
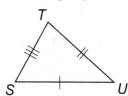

---

similar figures Two figures are similar if one can be obtained from the other by a series of rigid motions (translations, reflections or rotations) and/or dilations. These figures have the same shape and congruent corresponding angles, and all corresponding lengths are proportional. (Note that congruent figures are also considered to be similar.)

Example:

$\square ABCD \sim \square EFGH$

$\angle A \cong \angle E, \angle B \cong \angle F, \angle C \cong \angle G, \angle D \cong \angle H$

$\dfrac{AB}{EF} = \dfrac{BC}{FG} = \dfrac{CD}{GH} = \dfrac{DA}{HE}$

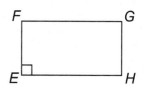

similar triangles Triangles with congruent corresponding angles that have the same shape, but not necessarily the same size. Corresponding sides of similar triangles are in proportion and corresponding angles are congruent.

Example:

$\triangle PQR \sim \triangle STU$

$\angle P \cong \angle S, \angle Q \cong \angle T, \angle R \cong \angle U$

$\dfrac{PQ}{ST} = \dfrac{QR}{TU} = \dfrac{RP}{US}$

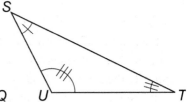

slide (translation) The movement of every point in an object or figure the same distance in the same direction.

Example:

$\triangle ABC$ is translated to $\triangle A'B'C'$.

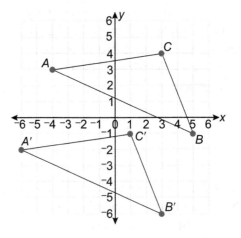

sphere A three-dimensional shape which consists of all points in space that are equidistant from a fixed point called the center. The distance is the radius of the sphere.

Example:

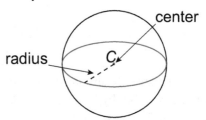

straight angle An angle with measure of 180 degrees.

Example:

$m\angle ABC = 180°$

substitution property of equality The property stating that if two objects are equal, then they can be substituted for each other.

Example:

If $a = b$, then a can be substituted for b in any expression or equation, and vice versa.

If $m\angle 1 + m\angle 2 = 105°$ and $\angle 1 \cong \angle 3$, then $m\angle 3 + m\angle 2 = 105°$.

---

supplementary angles Two angles whose measures have a sum of 180 degrees.

Example:

$m\angle A + m\angle B = 180°$

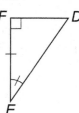

---

symbol "$\cong$" Congruent.

Example:

$\triangle ABC \cong \triangle DEF$ is read "triangle ABC is congruent to triangle DEF."

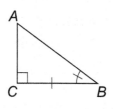

---

symbol "$\parallel$" Parallel.

Example:

$a \parallel b$ is read "a is parallel to b."

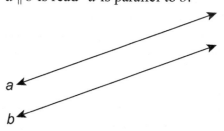

---

symbol "$\perp$" Perpendicular.

$l \perp m$ is read "l is perpendicular to m."

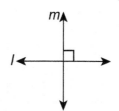

symbol "~" Similar.

Example:

$\triangle PQR \sim \triangle STU$ is read "triangle *PQR* is similar to triangle *STU*."

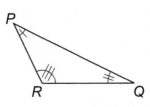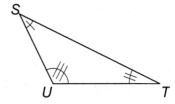

Third Angle Theorem The theorem that states that if two angles of a triangle are congruent to two angles of another triangle, then the third angles of the triangles are also congruent.

Example:

In any $\triangle ABC$ and $\triangle DEF$:

If m$\angle A$ = m$\angle D$ and m$\angle B$ = m$\angle E$, then m$\angle C$ = m$\angle F$.

---

transformation The movement of all points of a figure in a plane according to the same operation.

Example:

See translation, rotation, reflection and dilation. These are all transformations.

---

translation (slide) The movement of every point in an object or figure the same distance in the same direction.

Example:

$\triangle ABC$ is translated to $\triangle A'B'C'$.

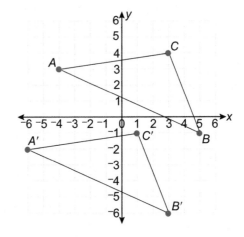

---

transversal A line that crosses two or more lines.

Example:

Line *l* is a transversal of *q*, *r* and *s*.

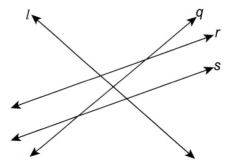

Triangle Sum Theorem The theorem that states that the sum of the measures of the angles in any triangle is 180 degrees.

Example:
In any $\triangle ABC$:

$m\angle A + m\angle B + m\angle C = 180°.$

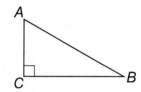

trigonometry The branch of mathematics that deals with the properties of triangles.

turn (rotation) A transformation that turns a figure about a given point in a specific direction and angle.

Example:
The figure at the top is a 90° counterclockwise rotation of the figure at the bottom around the vertex of the turn angle.

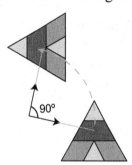

vertical angles Two non-adjacent angles formed by the intersection of two lines. Vertical angles have equal measures.

Example:
$\angle 1$ and $\angle 3$ are vertical angles. $\angle 2$ and $\angle 4$ are also vertical angles.

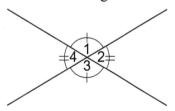

volume The amount of space contained in a three-dimensional solid, expressed in cubic units.

Example:

The volume of this sphere is $\frac{4}{3}\pi r^3$.

The volume of this rectangular prism is 60 cm³.

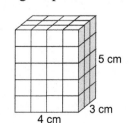

Lesson 1.1

Parallel Lines and Angles

Page 4, Question 5e: Notice that some of the pairs of supplementary angles do not form straight lines since they are not placed together. However, if placed adjacent to one another, they could form a straight line.

On Your Own

Page 8, Question 3: There are six pairs.

Page 8, Question 6a: First look at parallel sides $\overline{AB}$ and $\overline{CD}$ with $\overline{AD}$ as the transversal. Now find another pair of parallel sides and a transversal.

Page 10, Question 12b: Look up the definition of an exterior angle of a triangle in a mathematics dictionary, and compare it to your explanation.

Lesson 1.2

Proving the Triangle Sum Theorem

Page 14, Question 3c: What is the sum of the measures of angles 3, 4 and 5? What type of angles are ∠1 and ∠4? Angles 2 and 5?

On Your Own

Page 18, Question 2: Draw a diagonal within the quadrilateral.

On Your Own

Page 18, Question 3c: The angles opposite congruent sides are also congruent. In the figure, angle *B* is opposite side *AC* and angle *C* is opposite side *AB*. So ∠*B* ≅ ∠*C*.

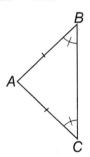

Lesson 1.3

Finding the Sum of the Measures of Angles in Polygons

Page 24, Question 6: *Do* is a prefix for *two*. Find out how many sides a dodecagon has by looking in a math dictionary or using the Internet.

On Your Own

Page 26, Question 7: Remember that a circle has 360°. In this case, square tiles work because 4 • 90° = 360°.

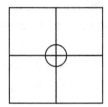

Lesson 2.1

Investigation 2: Side-Angle-Side Property

Page 39, Question 7: Look at the angle measures between the corresponding congruent sides.

On Your Own

Page 43, Question 5b: When might two triangles need to be congruent in order to support a structure?

Page 45, Question 10: Use your AngLegs™ to create different types of quadrilaterals.

Page 45, Question 11: Experiment with your AngLegs™.

Lesson 2.2

Pentominoes

Page 52, Question 5: There are 12 possible pentominoes. Traditionally the pentominoes are named after the letters they most closely resemble: F, I, L, N, P, T, U, V, W, X, Y, and Z.

Lesson 3.1

Finding the Volume of Cylinders

Page 109, Question 4: Think of filling a rectangular box with cubes. Relate this to the formula for finding the volume of a rectangular prism.

On Your Own

Page 112, Question 9: 1 mile $=$ 5,280 feet

Lesson 3.3

A Closer Look at Spheres

Page 120, Question 1: Remember how you defined *circle*? Make use of the center of the sphere in your definition in a similar way.

The Volume of Spheres and Cylinders

Page 121, Question 5: Remember that the height of the cylinder is twice the length of the radius.

On Your Own

Page 123, Question 3c: Think about cutting off both ends of the watermelon and putting them together to form a sphere. What shape is left over?

Page 126, Question 11: First decide what you think the volume of an average scoop of ice cream might be.

Unit Study Guide

Section 3

Page 138, Question 16: See **On Your Own** Question 6 from Lesson 3.2 on p.116 to review what a yurt is.

Index

A

acute (See also *angles, triangles*), 35

alternate exterior angles (See also *angles*), 6, 29

alternate interior angles (See also *angles*), 6, 29

AngLegs™ (to measure angles) (See also *angles, Geometer's Sketchpad*), 3, 7, 40

Angle-Angle-Angle (AAA) Similarity Property (See also *angle, congruence, triangles*), 75, 101, 136, 140

Angle-Angle-Side (AAS) Theorem (See also *angle, congruence, triangles*), 74, 141

Angle-Angle (AA) Similarity Theorem (See also *angle, congruence, triangles*), 78, 101, 140

Angle-Side-Angle (ASA) Property (See also *angle, congruence, included side, triangles*), 41, 42, 74, 96, 135, 141

included side and, 41

angles (See also *AngLegs, corresponding parts, interior angle, intersecting lines, lines, similarity, Third Angle Theorem, triangles*)

acute, 35, 140

alternate exterior, 6, 29, 140

alternate interior, 6, 29, 140

AngLegs™ to measure, 3, 7

congruent, 40 (*marking*), 101

corresponding, 29, 34, 78, 101, 142

included, 39, 40, 41, 45

interior, 22, 25, 26

intersecting lines form, 2

parallel lines and, 4, 34

quadrilateral, 18

rotation and turn, 54

same-side interior, 6, 29

straight, 3

supplementary, 3, 29, 32

triangles, 14, 15, 78

vertical, 2, 29, 32

area

circle, 13

cylinder or cone surface, 118

surface (formula), 118

axes (See *coordinate grid*)

C

Cartesian coordinate system (See *coordinate plane*)

circle (See also *cylinder*), 107

circumference, 107, 113

diameter, 113

circumference (See also *circle*), 107, 113

cone (See also *volume*), 114, 115, 141

surface area, 118

volume, 115, 129, 130

congruence and congruent (See also *angles, corresponding parts, similarity, shapes, triangles*), 2, 36, 37, 40, 141

Angle-Angle-Angle (AAA) Similarity Property, 75

Angle-Angle-Side (AAS) Theorem, 74

Angle-Side-Angle (ASA) Property, 36, 74

figures, 141

included angle and, 40, 45

rotation and, 65

shapes, 55

Side-Angle-Side Property, 36, 74

Side-Side-Side (SSS) Theorem, 36

similar and, 75, 100

symbol for, 2, 151

triangles, 42, 81, 82, 95, 101

coordinate plane (See also *Cartesian coordinate system*), 62–73, 99, 100, 137

labeling axes, 62

plot (graph) points on, 62, 70, 98

polygon, 64, 98

reflecting and, 63, 64, 99, 100

rotations and, 99, 100

transformations on, 61, 100

triangles on, 66

corresponding (See also *angles, congruence, similarity, triangles*), 36

angles, 29, 34, 36, 37, 74, 142

sides, 36, 142

triangles, 78

cylinder (See also *circle*), 108, 128, 142

surface area, 118

volume, 128, 138

D

deductive reasoning (See *reasoning*)

diameter (of a circle) (See also *circle, circumference, pi(π)*), 113

dilation (See also *transformations*), 88, 143
    coordinate grid, 99, 100
    designing using, 90

E

enlargements (See *dilation*)

equiangular (See also *triangles*), 35, 143

equilateral (See also *triangles*), 35, 143
    triangle is also isosceles, 35

F

flip (reflection) (See also *transformations*), 143

formula
    angles of polygon, 22
    circumference, 107, 113
    surface area, 118
    volume of a cone, 129, 130
    volume of a cylinder, 128
    volume of a sphere, 130

G

games (See also *pentominoes*)
    Place the Pentominoes, 54

graphing points (See *coordinate plane*)

H

hemisphere (See also *sphere*), 121, 122, 143

I

image (See also *reflection, rotation, transformations, translation*), 48, 144

included angle (See also *angle, included side*), 39, 40, 144
    SAS Property requires, 45

included side (See also *angle, included angle*), 41, 144

inductive reasoning (See *reasoning*)

interior angle (See also *angle, polygon*), 22, 26
    of a polygon, 145
    sum of, 25

intersecting lines (See also *angles, lines, parallel*)
    form angles, 2

isosceles (See also *triangles*), 35
    equilateral triangle is also, 35
    triangle, 145

L

line of symmetry (See also *image, reflection, rotation, transformations translation*), 48, 50, 145

lines (See also *angles, parallel*), 4

M

measuring
    indirect, 144

O

obtuse (See also *angles, triangles*), 35, 145

P

parallel (See also *lines*), 4, 9, 145
    angles and, 34
    symbol, 151

pentominoes (See also *games*), 52, 54, 58, 146
    Place the Pentominoes, 54

perpendicular line intersection (See also *lines*), 146
    symbol, 151

pi (π) (See also *circle, circumference, diameter*), 107, 114, 146

plotting points (See *coordinate grid*)

polygons (See also *interior angle, shapes*)
    congruent, 96
    interior angles of, 25, 145
    plotting, 98
    reflection, 63
    regular, 24
    rotations, 64
    similar, 100

CPSIA information can be obtained at www.ICGtesting.com
Printed in the USA
LVOW02s2333160715

446374LV00004B/4/P

9 781465 212481